100 Notes – 100 Thoughts / 100 Notizen – 100 Gedanken | №081

Trash hacks

Einfälle statt Abfälle

dOCUMENTA (13)

HATJE CANTZ

② "Einfälle statt Abfälle"

Wir haben ein Wissen angehäuft zur Lösung "aller Probleme der Welt" und verbrauchen doch trotz modernster Spartechniken immer mehr? Wir sind immer unfähiger geworden, unser Leben selbst in die Hand zu nehmen. Konsum ist in Sauberdeutschland so bequem, weil er längst zu Lasten anderer Völker geht. Als braver Bürger schaue ich auf den Stromzähler und kaufe ein neues energiesparendes Gerät, statt das alte zu reparieren. Daß die Herstellung des neuen Gerätes oft weit mehr Energie fraß als es im Gebrauch gegenüber dem alten je sparen kann, zeigt mir der Zähler nicht, und schon gar nicht, ob ich das Gerät überhaupt wirklich brauche...

Im Großen geht's genau so: Die "Klimabilanz" Deutschlands berücksichtigt nur, was hier im Land an CO_2 ausgestoßen wurde. Aber die Schlote rauchen doch längst woanders! Die meisten energieintensiv und umweltzerstörend gewonnenen Rohstoffe importieren wir aus fernen Ländern, wälzen damit Schaden und Ausbeutung erstmal auf andere ab und machen hier nur den letzten Verarbeitungsschritt, damit "made in Germany" draufsteht - wenn wir nicht gleich das fertige Produkt importieren. Und der Müll? Wird gut versteckt, exportiert, oder wir heizen die Müllverbrennungsanlagen mit Plastik aus China, um in Deutschland Erdöl zu sparen. Das Wiederverwenden gebrauchter Gegenstände ist im System höchst unerwünscht, da schädlich für die deutsche Konjunktur...

Willst Du von alldem unabhängiger werden, kannst Du Dein Leben selbst gestalten. In Wohlstandsdeutschland liegt zwar viel im Müll, was Du "aus 2. Hand" benutzen oder umarbeiten kannst, das Ideal sollte aber sein, ohne Wohlstandsmüll direkt im Kreislauf der Natur zu leben. Wer für sich selber sorgt, weiß, wie viel er wofür verbraucht und kann das menschliche Maß leichter finden. Wer im Palast lebt und das Holz zum Heizen selber machen müßte, würde frieren, und wer die Energie zur Herstellung seiner Getränkedosen selbst erarbeiten müßte, verdurstet in 3 Tagen.

Bei "Energiewende" denkt man zuerst an Strom. Für Solarstrom muß ich Solarzellen kaufen, doch Windräder kann ich aus Holz und Schrott selber bauen - eine faszinierende Sache. Man sieht, hört und spürt, was passiert. Das Problem bleibt aber wie beim Solarstrom: Speicherung in Batterien, wegen höchstgiftiger Herstellung bitte nur vom Schrott! Froh sei, wer einen Bach in der Nähe hat - beim Wasserrad ist Stromspeicherung überflüssig, wir brauchen keine Batterie dafür.

Doch die aufgeregte Stromdebatte lenkt ab von dem, wofür wir 4 x mehr Energie verbrauchen: für Wärme. Ohne die geht's hierzulande ums Erfrieren, Strom ist dagegen Luxus. Aber Wärme schmeißen wir zum auf Kipp geöffneten Fenster raus: es bleibt ja warm, auch wenn wir nichts dafür tun, denn versteckt im Keller brüllt im Automatik-Brennwertkessel ein Höllenfeuer auf.

Also sparen wir doch Wärme und gewinnen sie am liebsten von der Sonne. Kollektoren gewinnen die Wärme direkt, ohne Umweg über Strom, und "ernten" über 1o x mehr Energie, als wenn wir den gleichen Aufwand in eine Solarstromanlage gesteckt hätten. Die Speicherung in einem gut gedämmten Behälter ist denkbar einfach. Der Selbstbau von Sonnenkollektoren, die ohne Strom, Pumpen und Technik bestens funktionieren, könnte längst Volkswissen sein. Naja, der Kauf von Kollektoren wird inzwischen sogar auch ein bißchen gefördert, der Selbstbau natürlich nicht...

Fast noch einfacher das Heizen: Habe ich eine während der kalten Zeit sonnenbeschienene Wand, kann ich sie durch vorgesetzte Altglasscheiben zum Sonnenwärme-Speicherkollektor verwandeln und so die Heizperiode um mindestens 4-8 Wochen verkürzen. Ganz ohne Technik! Für den Sommer ist noch eine biologische Regelung durch Schatten von Laubbäumen (Walnuß!) oder baulich durch ein Vordach nötig.

In sonniger Lage kann man Häuser so (um)bauen, daß die Sonne sie komplett heizt, doch die meisten Häuser stehen dafür zu ungünstig. Wo wir noch mit Feuer heizen müssen, bleiben wir mit Holz im Naturkreislauf, so lange wir weniger verbrennen als nachwächst.

Auf Pelletsfabriken, Spezialheizkessel, Pumpen, Gebläse, Lambdasonden, Abgasventilatoren, Rauchgasfilter, thermische Ablaufsicherungen etc.pp. können wir getrost verzichten. Sauber, effektiv und komfortabel heizen wir schon mit einem aus Ziegeln und Lehm selbstgemauerten Grundofen: 1 Stunde Feuer, 12 Stunden Speicherwärme, oder größer und durch mehrere Räume gebaut als Grundofen fürs ganze Haus mit 24 Stunden Dauerwärme.

Die käufliche Öko-Technik, egal ob Holzheizung, Wärmepumpe oder Solaranlage, will uns abhängig halten, ist undurchschaubar aufgebaut, nur vom Fachbetrieb zu installieren und zu warten, und wenn der Strom mal ausbleibt, versagt alles, wir müssen trotz öko-dernier-cri frieren und haben kein Warmwasser. Moderne Kompliziertheit puscht den Wirkungsgrad zwar vordergründig noch ein paar Prozent hoch, aber daß Kühltürme dampfen und Atommeiler strahlen müssen, weil die Prozente mit Stromeinsatz erkauft wurden, mißt niemand.
Ebenso wie man lieber nicht fragt, wie viel an Energie zum Bau der Anlage und zur Gewinnung der industriellen Rohstoffe dafür verpraßt und wie sehr die Umwelt dabei zerstört wurde. Ich begann, Ökotechnik zu entwickeln, als es noch keine zu kaufen gab, und ich weiß, warum ich auf dem einfachen Weg geblieben bin.

Sehr viel Energie verbrauchen wir auch, um uns selber fortzubewegen - mit Autos, die nicht nur Treibstoff schlucken, Lärm verbreiten und Luft verpesten, sondern für die auch viel Land zugeteert wird, die umweltzerstörend hergestellt und verschrottet werden. Aber schließlich schafft die Autoindustrie "jeden 7. Arbeitsplatz"... Es liegt an uns selbst, wie wir unser Leben einrichten, mit langen Wegen oder kurzen, Streß oder Zeit. Auf kürzeren Wegen können wir vieles zu Fuß oder mit dem Rad schaffen und sogar große, schwere Dinge mit einem aus Schrottfahrrädern gebauten Lastenrad transportieren. Und - wir haben Zeit, weil wir nicht mehr fürs Auto schuften müssen!

Doch geht es eigentlich nur um Energie im technischen Sinne? Ist unser Leben nicht mehr? Ist unser eigentliches Ziel nicht einfach, glücklich leben zu können? Und dies auch den Generationen nach uns zu ermöglichen? Daß unsere Lebensfreude steigt, wenn wir immer "mehr" kaufen, haben, verbrauchen, das haben uns diejenigen von Kind auf eingeredet, die mit unserem Leben Profit machen wollen (und müssen, weil sie ein System mit Zwang zum "Wirtschaftswachstum" betreiben). Mehr konsumieren macht aber immer unselbständiger, erzeugt den Streß, dem Geld hinterherzujagen und läßt immer weniger Chancen, sein Leben selbst zu bestimmen. Schritt für Schritt vergessen wir die Fähigkeit, elementare Dinge selbst zu tun. Beispiel: Jeder hier trägt Schuhe. Wer kann noch selber welche machen?

Von Kind auf lernten wir die Konsum-Lebensweise, unsere Hände greifen automatisch zum Warmwasserhahn und zum Lichtschalter, werfen weg, ohne daß wir eine Spur dabei nachdenken, warum wir das gerade tun. Zeitlebens antrainierte Gewohnheiten zu ändern ist schwer, aber nötig, denn "öko" kann man nicht kaufen, man muß es selber leben, sonst ist es nur ökonsum!

Ich behaupte, unsere Lebensfreude kann sehr steigen, wenn wir mehr Bereiche unseres Lebens selbst gestalten können, und das ideal im Kreislauf der Natur. Wir sind nicht nur zum Geldverdienen da! Wo kommt unsere tägliche Nahrung her? Kann ich selbst Früchte sammeln oder einen Garten bestellen? Muß ich das, was die Fruchtbarkeit der Erde erhalten soll, im modernen Abwassersystem energieaufwendig zu Gift verarbeiten lassen? Ein Kompost-Klo schließt wieder den Kreislauf der Natur und macht die Kunstdüngerfabriken für mich überflüssig.

Muß ich mir diktieren lassen, die Kleidung zu kaufen wie die anderen sie tragen? Ich kann auch selber nähen: statt so viel Kleidung lieber meine besondere, und Löcher und bunte Flicken haben ihre Geschichte. Muß ich Plastik oder importierte Baumwolle tragen und mühsam waschen, wo doch Wolle von hier besser wärmt, weniger Dreck annimmt und leichter zu waschen ist?

Allerlei Gebrauchsgerät selbst herzustellen kann auch große Freude machen, Löffel schnitzen statt WMF-Besteck kaufen, Schüsseln aus Lehm töpfern, Becher aus Wegwerfflaschen schneiden, Möbel aus Knickrodeholz bauen und so weiter, all dies gibt mir die Möglichkeit, nicht nur den praktischen Zweck zu erfüllen, sondern meine eigene, individuelle, künstlerische Gestaltung mit einzubringen. Und was ich selbst gebaut habe, habe ich auch verstanden, kann es jederzeit selbst reparieren, verbessern oder neu bauen. Unsere Gefühle, Freude, Dankbarkeit können wir auch ausdrücken wenn wir selber singen oder Instrumente spielen, ohne den Sänger aus der elektronischen Dose.

Brauchen wir eigentlich all diese Geräte und Produkte unserer Wohlstandswelt? Ich behaupte mal, jedes zweite ist völlig unnütz und dient oft nur dazu, ein anderes unnützes Produkt zu pflegen und so weiter. Wir lassen riesige Sachen-Aufbewahrungsbehälter aus Beton, Stahl und Kunststoff mit Hightech-Energierückgewinnung bauen und heizen, und nebenbei sind dann auch ein paar Quadratmeter Platz für uns selber drin. Eigentlich könnten wir auch aus Lehm und Stroh im menschlichen Maß selber bauen, aber das gilt dann als, naja, "weniger repräsentativ".

Wie viele Kinder hier bekommen kaum noch Zeit und Gelegenheit, frei in der Natur zu spielen, mit gefundenen Dingen phantasievoll zu experimentieren und praktische Tätigkeiten selbst auszuprobieren! Das Bildungssystem verordnet den Kinsie zu eher unselbständig funktionierenden Zahnrädchen im Wirtschaftsgetriebe trainiert und ihnen das "Abenteuer Selbermachen" vorenthält.

Stattdessen machen wir uns von der elektronischen Krücke "Computer" abhängig, wir schütten uns mit Informationen aus dem Internet zu und merken nicht, wie uns dabei die Zeit zerrinnt, irgendetwas selbst in die Tat umzusetzen. Virtuelle Äpfel kann man nicht essen, und pflanzt der Computer etwa Kartoffeln oder strickt er Socken?

Seit meiner Schulzeit arbeite ich an alternativen Wegen und gebe bewährte "Rezepte" als Anregung zum Nachbauen und Weiterentwickeln in meiner Reihe "Einfälle statt Abfälle" heraus. Keine teuren, nur fürs Fachpublikum lesbaren Fachbücher, sondern ich zeichne und erkläre anschaulich zum Nachbau mit einfachsten Mitteln. Ich lasse im Kleinformat drucken, weil es weniger Papier verbraucht und auch noch billiger wird. So ein eingerahmter [Sonne-Heft 1] Hinweis auf den Seiten dieses "Notizbuches" nennt das Heft der Reihe "Einfälle statt Abfälle" zum jeweiligen Thema.

Alle "Einfälle"-Hefte sowie eine Titelliste sind bei mir direkt erhältlich (Selbstverlag, Christian Kuhtz, Hagebuttenstr. 23, 24113 Kiel, oder über Fax o431/32oo686), während im Internet auch unter meinem Namen oder "Markennamen" viele Raubdrucke verkauft werden: ich habe keine Internetseite. Der Kauf von Raubdrucken entzieht mir den Lohn und mindert so die Möglichkeit, weitere "Einfälle statt Abfälle" zu entwickeln.

Einfälle statt Abfälle Verlag

Werkstatt für ökologische Technik
Christian Kuhtz
Hagebuttenstr. 23, 24113 Kiel

Introduction

Have we amassed the knowledge to solve "all the world's problems" only to drive up consumption, despite our modern efficiency technologies? We have become increasingly incapable of taking charge of our own lives. The only reason consumption has become so easy for so long in our green Germany is because the price for that consumption has been paid by other peoples. As an upstanding citizen, I mind my electricity meter and buy myself a new, energy-efficient appliance instead of repairing the old one. But the meter doesn't show me that it often takes far more energy to manufacture the new appliance than I could possibly ever save by replacing the old one—and the meter will certainly never tell me whether I even really need this new gadget.

The big picture is no different: Germany's "climate balance" only takes into account carbon emissions here in Germany. But for years, stacks in other lands have continued to belch out their smoke. The raw materials whose production is most energy intensive and environmentally destructive we import from faraway lands. We push the damage and the exploitation onto others, while we perform the final manufacturing step here, so that we can claim "Made in Germany"—if, that is, we don't import the finished product in its entirety. And what of the waste? It is well hidden, exported—or we heat waste-incineration plants with plastic from China to conserve oil in Germany. Reuse of cast-off products is highly undesirable in the system. That, after all, is a threat to the German economy.

Do you want to be more independent; can you take your life into your own hands? While many things can be found in wealthy Germany's trash that can be used secondhand or made into something useful, the ideal should be to live directly within the cycle of nature without reliance on the cast-offs of the wealthy. A person who supplies his own needs knows how much effort is required and for what purpose, and can more easily find a human measure. A person living in a palace who had to chop all of the wood to heat it would soon freeze, and if a person had to expend his own energy to make his drink bottles he would be dead of thirst in three days.

When it comes to the "energy revolution," most people think first of electricity. To get solar power, I first have to buy solar cells, but I can make windmills with my own hands out of wood and trash—it's fascinating to think about. You can see, feel, and hear what's going on. But the problem is the same as with solar power: battery storage (please only use salvaged batteries due to highly poisonous manufacturing techniques). You're fortunate if you've got a nearby stream; with a waterwheel, energy storage is redundant.

But the heated debate over the power supply diverts attention from the source of four times more energy consumption: heat. Without it, we'd all freeze here in Germany. By comparison, electricity is a luxury. But we dump heat out of windows that are tilted open. Hey, it's still warm regardless, because there's a hellfire raging in our thermostat-controlled furnace in the cellar.

Thus, we should do something to save heat energy and production—if possible, we should get it from the sun. Collectors gather heat directly without the intermediary of electricity, and harvest more than ten times as much energy as if the same amount of money had been spent on a solar-power system. Storing the heat in a well-insulated container is a simple matter. An understanding of how to build a solar collector that works perfectly without any electricity, pumps, or fancy technology could have been common knowledge long ago. Yes, you can get a small subsidy to buy collectors—of course, there are no subsidies if you build them yourself.

Space heating with the sun is even easier. If you've got a wall with the sun shining on it during the cold months, you can install salvaged windows in front of it and convert it into a solar-thermal collector and shorten the heating season by at least four to eight weeks—no gadgets necessary. For the summer, you can control the climate either biologically—using the shade of leafy trees (walnuts)—or by building an awning.

In sunny locations you can build or rebuild houses such that they are completely heated by the sun. Unfortunately, most houses are not favorably oriented. In places where we still have to heat with fire, wood allows us to stay within the natural cycle, as long as more trees grow back than are burned.

We can confidently abstain from pelletizing plants, fancy furnaces, blowers, pumps, exhaust fans, oxygen sensors, thermal-overload devices, exhaust-gas filters, etc. We can heat our houses cleanly, effectively, and comfortably with nothing more than a stove homemade from bricks and clay—one hour of fire, twelve hours of stored heat—or we can extend the system to several rooms with a wood stove that heats the house around the clock.

The eco-gadgets available for sale—the wood-heating systems, heat pumps, solar-thermal systems—all aim to keep us dependent. The designs are not transparent, and they can only be installed and maintained by specialists. And if the power should go out, everything fails—despite the latest eco-gadget, you still freeze and have no hot water. On the face of it, modern complexity pushes efficiency a couple of percentage points higher, but the cooling towers continue steaming and the nuclear plants continue irradiating because nobody is keeping track of the fact that the cost of that couple of points is the use of electricity, lots of electricity. In the same way, people choose not to think about how much energy is gobbled up to build a renewable-energy system and to obtain the industrial raw materials for it, or how the environment is annihilated in the process. I started developing ecological technology before it was available on the market, and I know why I've stayed on the path of simplicity.

We also use a lot of energy to move ourselves from place to place in cars, which not only guzzle fuel and pollute the air, but also for whose sake so much land is covered with asphalt, which is produced and disposed of in environmentally destructive ways. But wait, the automobile industry creates "one in every seven jobs."

It is our responsibility and our responsibility alone to organize our lives—we are free to choose long distances or short ones, stress or time. We can get a lot of things done by walking or cycling short distances, and we can even move large heavy objects with a cargo bicycle made from old junked bikes. And we have time to do so because we no longer have to bust our humps in servitude to our cars!

But is energy, in the technical sense, really the issue? Don't our lives consist of more than that? Isn't our real goal simply to live happily and to enable subsequent generations to do the same? Our happiness increases when we buy, possess, and consume "more"—that is what those who seek to exploit our lives as a means to profit have convinced us from our childhood on (in fact, they have to preach this because they have espoused a system that demands "economic growth"). But more consumption increases dependency, creates stress from chasing money, and cuts us off from opportunities to live our lives deliberately. Step-by-step, we are losing the capability to do simple things for ourselves. For example, everybody here in Germany wears shoes; how many of us know how to make them?

From our childhood on, we have learned the consumer lifestyle. Our hands automatically reach for the hot-water tap and the light switch; we throw things away without the least thought about why. Lifelong habits are hard to change, but we have to change because ecological living cannot be bought. We have to live it; otherwise, it's nothing but eco-consumerism.

I submit that the quality of our lives can improve considerably if we are willing to take control of more areas of our lives and, ideally, to do it within the cycle of nature. We were not created to earn money! Where does our daily nourishment come from? Can't I collect fruit myself or plant a garden? Must I take what should be returned to the earth to make it fruitful and allow it to be processed through the modern wastewater system, at a vast expense of energy, into poison? A composting toilet closes the cycle of nature and makes synthetic-fertilization factories useless to me.

Do I have to allow people to dictate to me that I must buy clothing that is the same as what other people are wearing? I, too, can sew. Instead of having a lot of clothing I prefer to have my own special clothing—each hole and colorful patch has its own story. Do I have to wear plastic or imported cotton and expend great effort washing it here, where local wool provides better warmth, does not get dirty as easily, and is easier to wash?

Making all kinds of useful things for yourself can also give great pleasure: carving a spoon instead of buying WMF flatware, throwing your own clay bowls, making glasses out of discarded bottles, making furniture out of salvaged wood from forest clear-cuts, and so on. All this gives me the opportunity not only to fulfill the practical goal but also to exercise my own, individual artistic sense. And what I have built myself, I also understand that whenever I want I can repair it, improve it, or rebuild it. We can express our feelings, our joy, and our thankfulness by singing or playing instruments without the need for the singer in the electronic box. Do we really need all of these devices and products, our world of prosperity? I submit that every second gadget is completely useless and often merely serves a further useless product, and so on.

We build and heat huge containers of steel, concrete, and plastic in which to store our things, containers with high-tech energy-recovery systems that, almost as an afterthought, also contain a few square meters of space for us to live in. Actually, we could build a house ourselves on a more human scale from clay and straw, but that would not be considered "prestigious." How many of our children still have the time and opportunity to play outside in nature, imaginatively experiment with found objects, and try their hand at practical activities for themselves? From their youth on, the educational system prescribes children a regimen of activities that train them to be dependent cogs in the economic machine and deprive them of the adventure of doing things themselves.

Instead, we have made ourselves dependent on the electronic crutch, the computer. As we pour ourselves a generous portion of information from the Internet, time in which we could actually do a real thing melts away. You cannot eat a virtual apple. Can your computer plant potatoes or knit a sock?

Ever since I was a schoolboy, I have been coming up with alternative ways to do things and providing proven "recipes" to inspire others to build and further develop these ideas in my series, "Trash Hacks." These are not expensive technical publications that only experts can understand. Rather, I illustrate and clearly explain how to build with the simplest means. I print these leaflets in a small format because it uses less paper and is cheaper. A title in a box like this, [Sonne-Heft 1], shows the name and the corresponding subject of the volume in the "Trash Hacks" series. All of the "Trash Hacks" volumes, as well as a complete list of titles, are available directly from me (Selbstverlag Christian Kuhtz, Hagebuttenstr. 23, 24113, Kiel). I do not have a website. Many pirated copies are available on the Internet under my name and other "brand names," but the sale of pirated copies denies me compensation for my work and limits my ability to develop further volumes of "Trash Hacks."

Kleinstes Windrad für den ersten Bastelspaß!

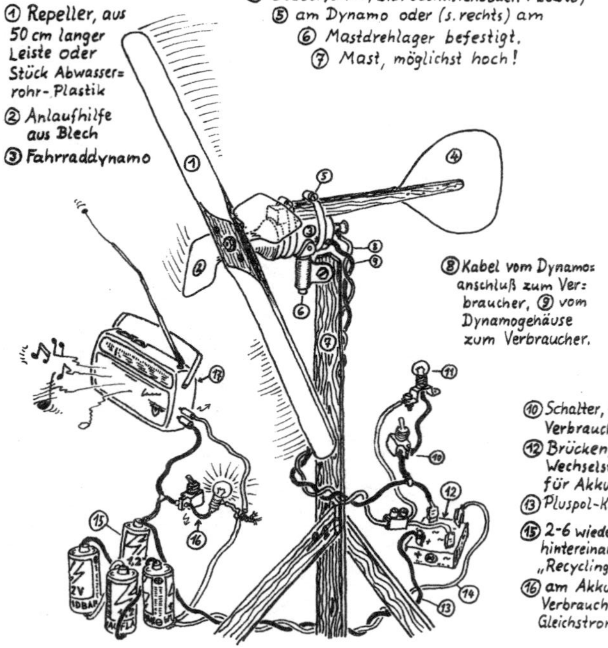

⑩ Schalter, für einen direkt angeschlossenen Verbraucher ⑪, z.B. Glühbirne
⑫ Brückengleichrichter, macht aus dem Wechselstrom vom Dynamo Gleichstrom für Akkus und Geräte mit Elektronik
⑬ Pluspol-Kabel ⑭ Minuspol-Kabel
⑮ 2-6 wiederaufladbare Akkuzellen hintereinander geschaltet. Öko: aus „Recycling"-Boxen in Läden sammeln!
⑯ am Akkustromkreis angeschlossener Verbraucher, ⑰ Verbraucher nur für Gleichstrom, z.B. Radio, LED, Walkman...

Einfachstes Windrad mit Fahrraddynamo, 50-cm-Repeller.

Small windmill – an introduction to the joy of tinkering

1	Rotor made from a 50 cm piece of waste wood or PVC drainpipe
2	Sheet-metal start-up assist | 3 | Bicycle dynamo
4	Wind vane, e.g. fruit crate bottom + shaft
5	attached to dynamo or (see drawing to the right) | 6 | on the mast bearing
7	Mast, as tall as possible!
8	Cable from the dynamo to the consumer | 9 | and the dynamo housing to the consumer
10	Switch for directly connected device | 11 | e.g. lamp
12	Bridge rectifier, converts the alternating current from the dynamo into direct current for rechargeable batteries and devices for DC current only
13	positive and | 14 | negative electric wires
15	2-6 rechargeable batteries connected in series.

Eco-tip: collect them from recycling boxes in stores!

16	Device connected to the battery circuit,
17	Device for DC current only, e.g. radio, led, Walkman...

Windkraft-Heft 1.

Profile 1:1 zum Abpausen
1:1 patterns for tracing

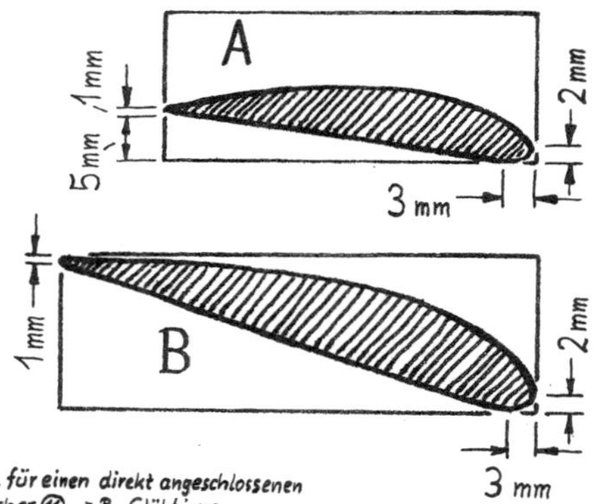

Repeller 50 cm ∅, Bau aus Holz — Construction of a wooden rotor blade (50 cm ∅)

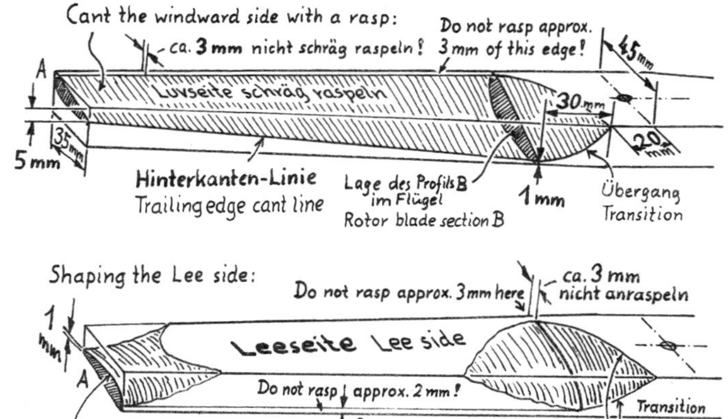

Profil an der Flügelspitze so raspeln: A – 2 mm nicht anraspeln! – Übergang – und am „1-mm-Meßpunkt" so: B.
Rasp the tip of the blade like this: A --- and like this (B) at the 1 mm measuring point.

Mast-Drehlager und Befestigung.
Bearing on top of the mast pipe, mount.

Auch ein „Rückweg-Kabel" zum Gehäuse legen, den Rückweg-Strom nur übers Lager leiten bringt oft Wackelkontakte!
Second wire connected to dynamo housing, otherwise the bearing may cause intermittent current!

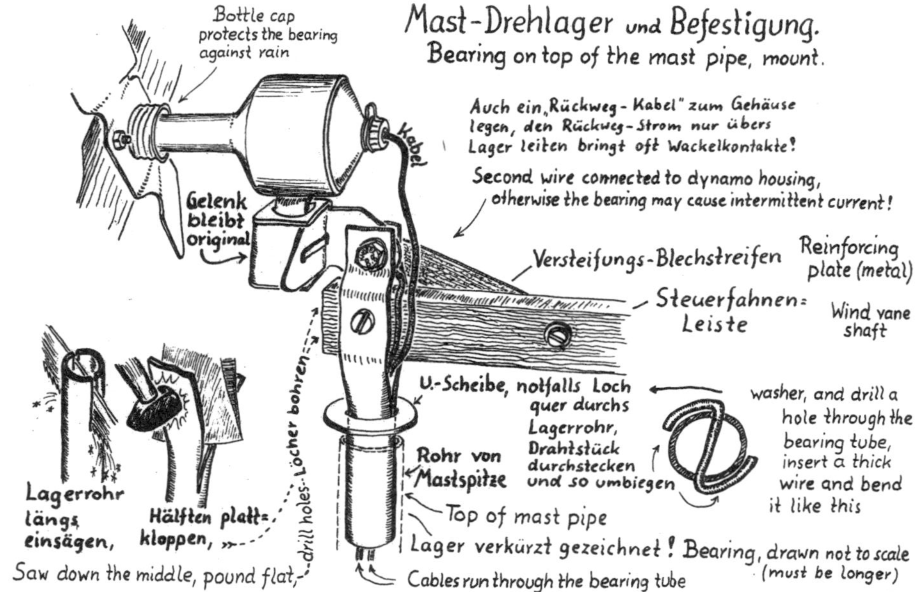

⑥ Leistungsfähiges Windrad mit Direktantrieb, ohne Getriebe!

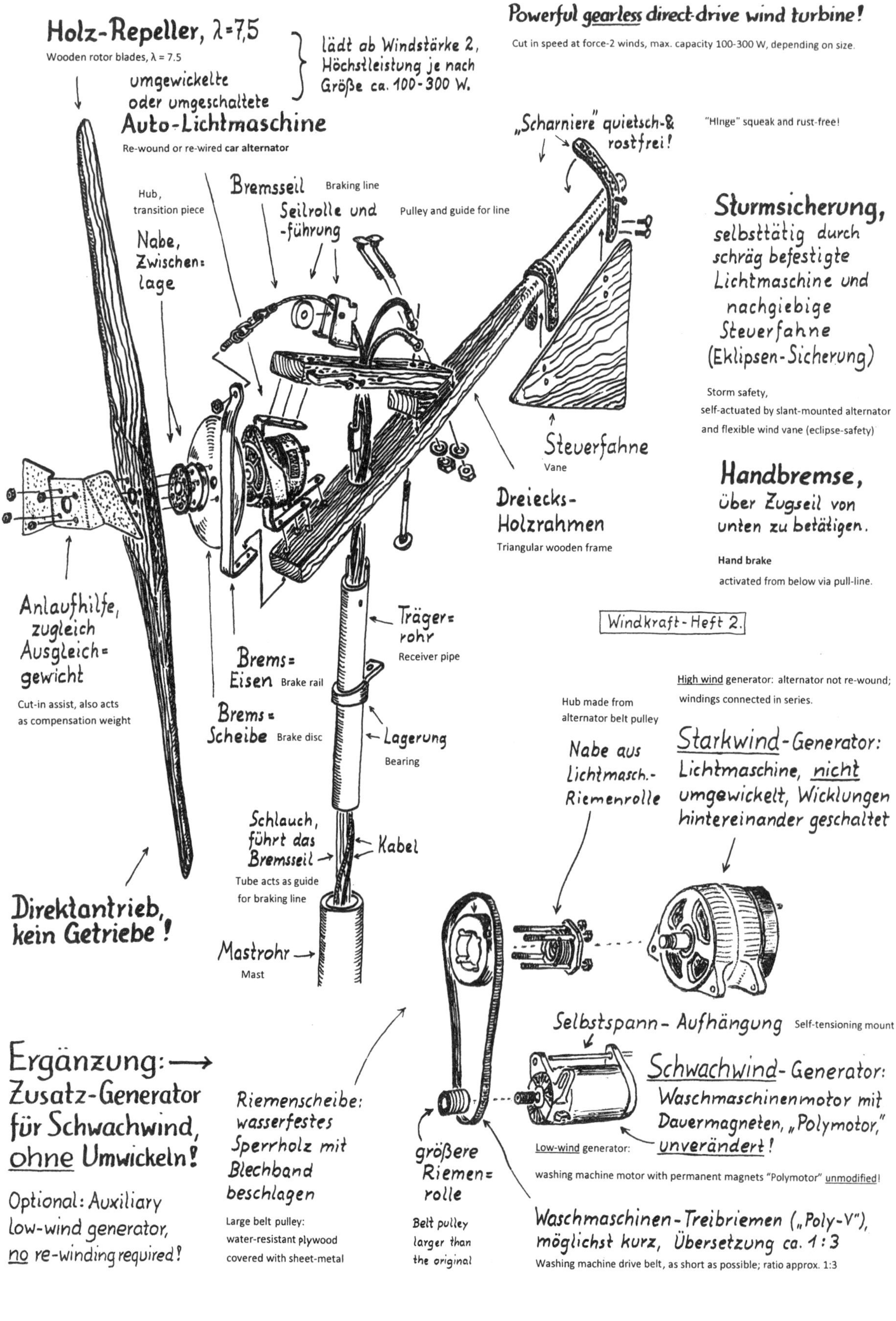

7

Größere Windrad-Bauart,
erstmals gebaut 1984.

Larger windmill-design, first built 1984.

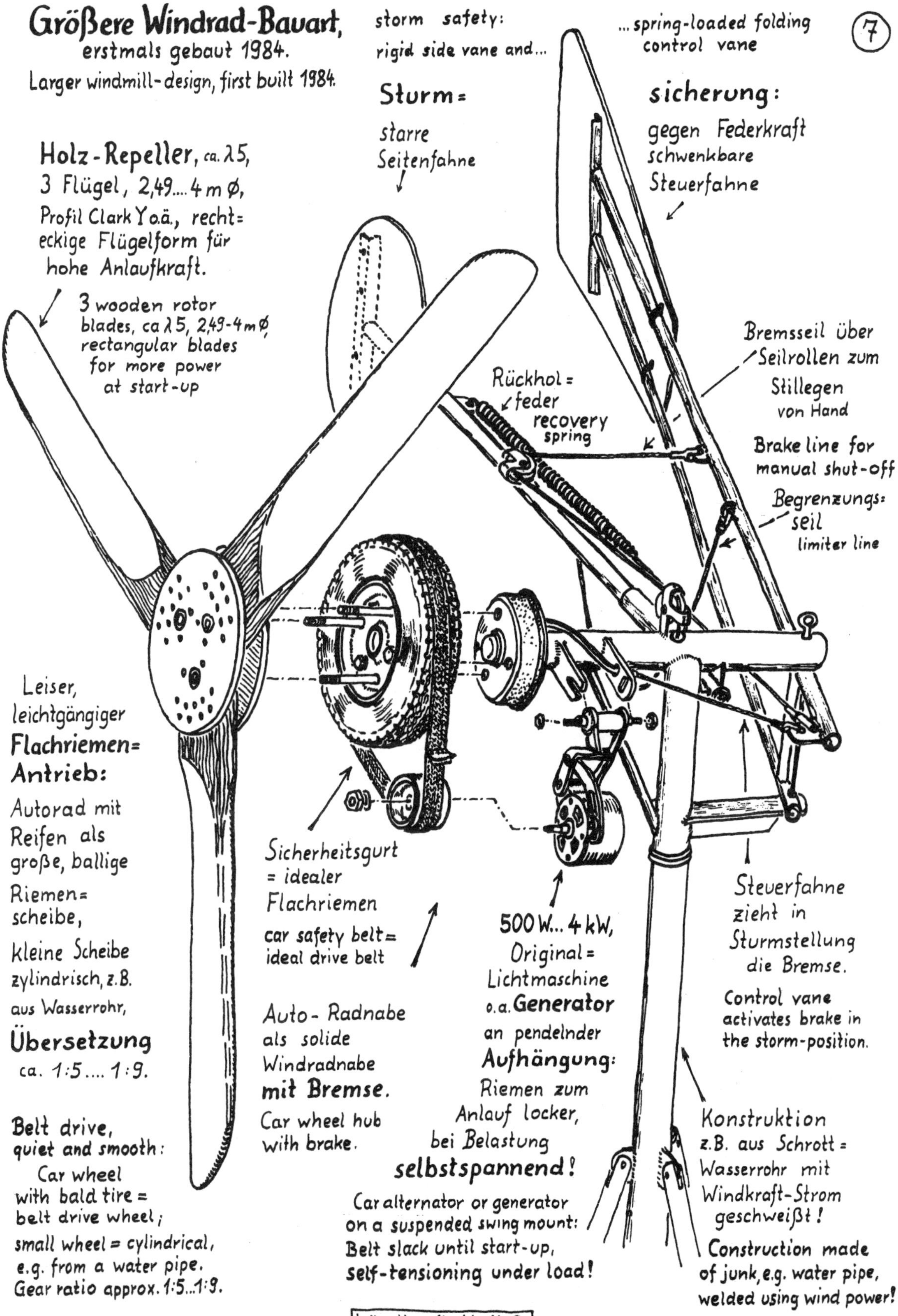

Das Strom-Floß!

Ein „unterschlächtiges Wasserrad", einfachst aus Fahrradschrott & Holz gebaut. Schwimmt angetäut auf dem Bach, schwankender Wasserstand egal. Fast keine Störung von Bachlauf und Natur! 2 Fahrrad-Hinterräder mit Wasserrohr als Achse verbunden. Generator + Getriebe ideal von Schrott-Mofa/Moped. Gibt dauernd Strom, auch ohne Batterie!

The Power Pontoon!

An undershot waterwheel easily built from junked bicycles and wood. The wheel floats, moored to the creek bed and is unaffected by fluctuating water levels. Almost no impact on creek flow or nature! Two bicycle rear wheels connected by a water pipe as an axle. The generator and transmission of a junked moped produce constant current — no batteries needed!

Unterschlächtiges Rad auch in langsam fließendem flachen Wasser

Undershot waterwheel also suitable for slow-moving flat water.

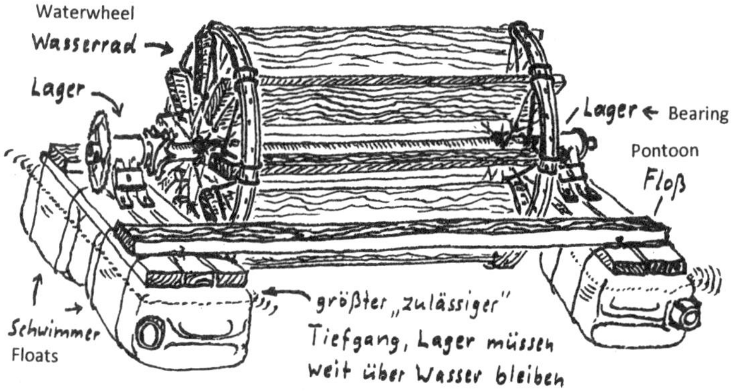

Greatest "acceptable" height - bearings must sit high above the water.

Pound flat the chain stays and down tube on the bottom bracket, bend and drill. Bolt onto pontoon.

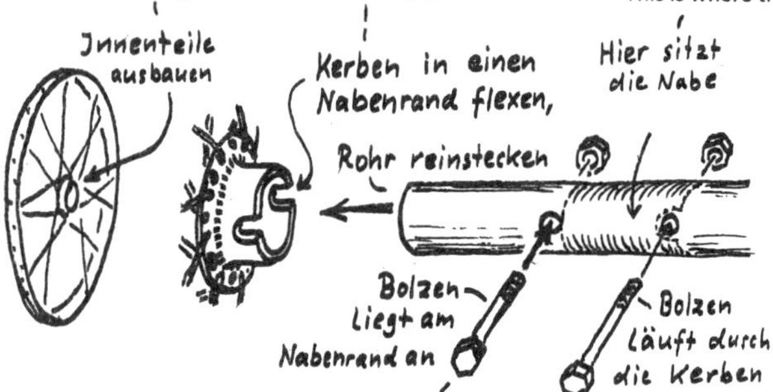

Bolt fits snug against the hub

Bolt fits into notches

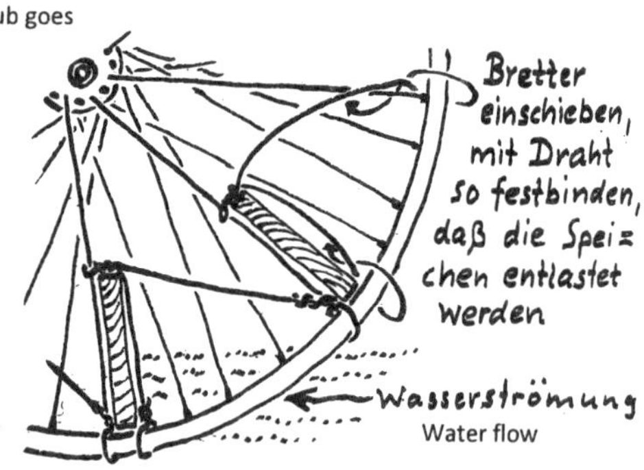

Slide boards in, secure them with wire to relieve stress on the spokes.

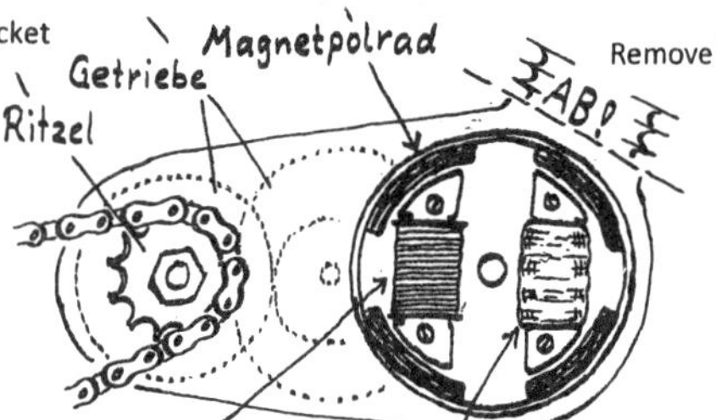

Lighting coil (thick wire)

Ignition coil (thin wire): replace wire or wrap thick wire on it.

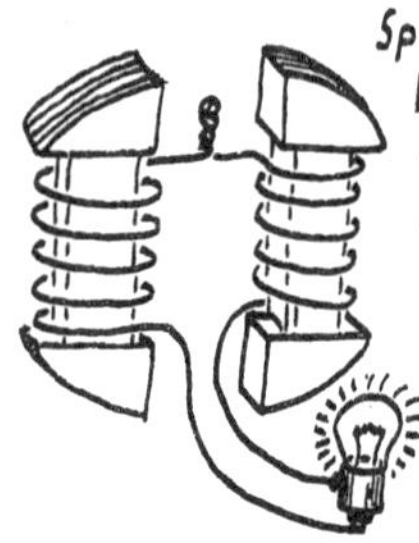

Wire the two coils together. If less current is generated than with a single coil, change the polarity of one of the coils. Generates alternating current, suitable for lamp. Add a bridge rectifier for battery charging.

Extrablatt

12-Volt-Selbstversorgerstrom ... was der alles kann! Selbst (um-)gebaute Geräte:

"All the things we can do with 12 volt self-generated power – DIY and modded devices"

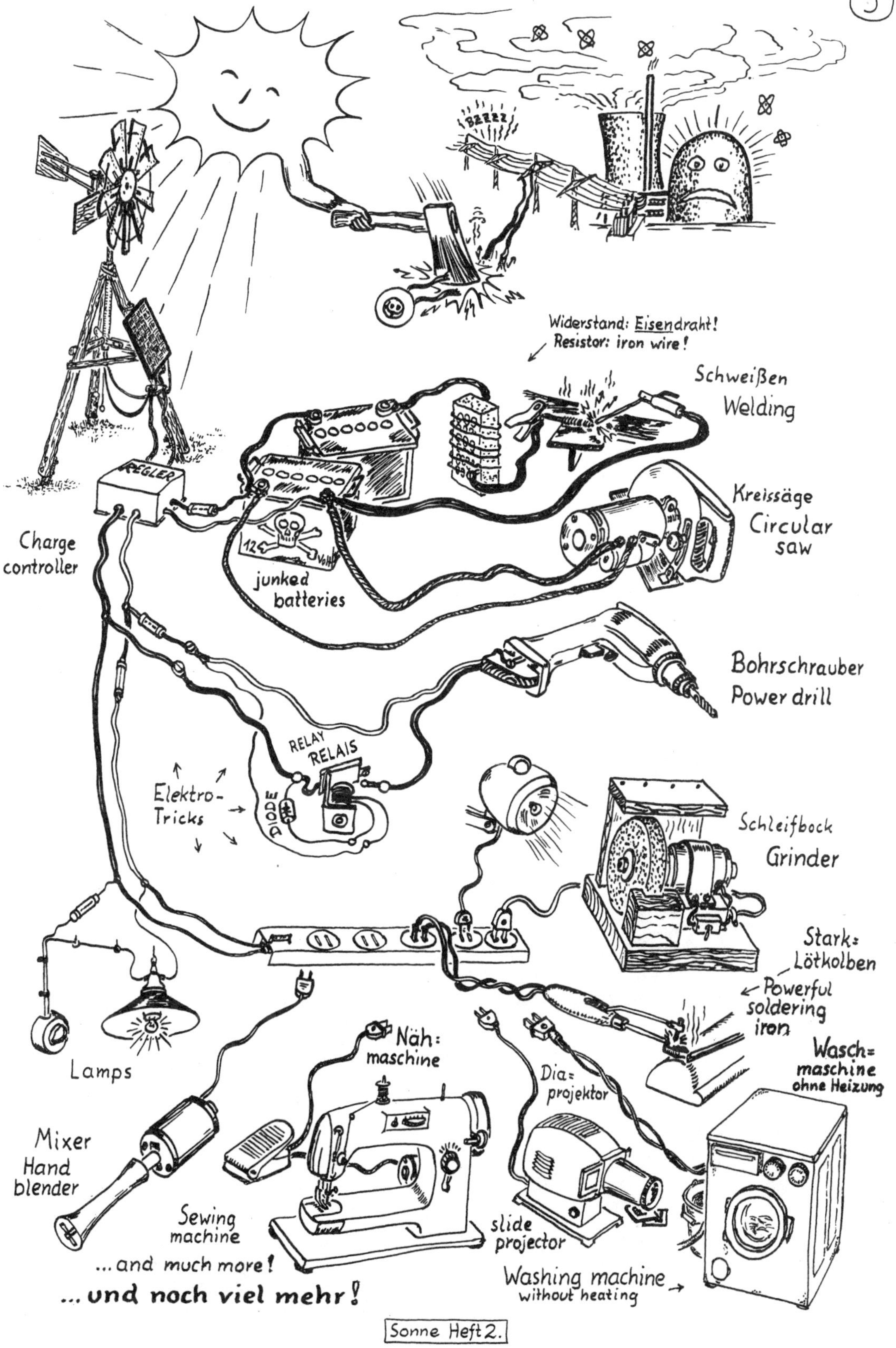

Sonne Heft 2.

Sonnenkollektor-Bauweise „öko-plus" !

Solar collector – "Eco-plus" design * with built-in wood protection *nearly chemical-free

***mit konstruktivem Holzschutz * fast ohne Chemieprodukte**

Sonne-Heft 1.

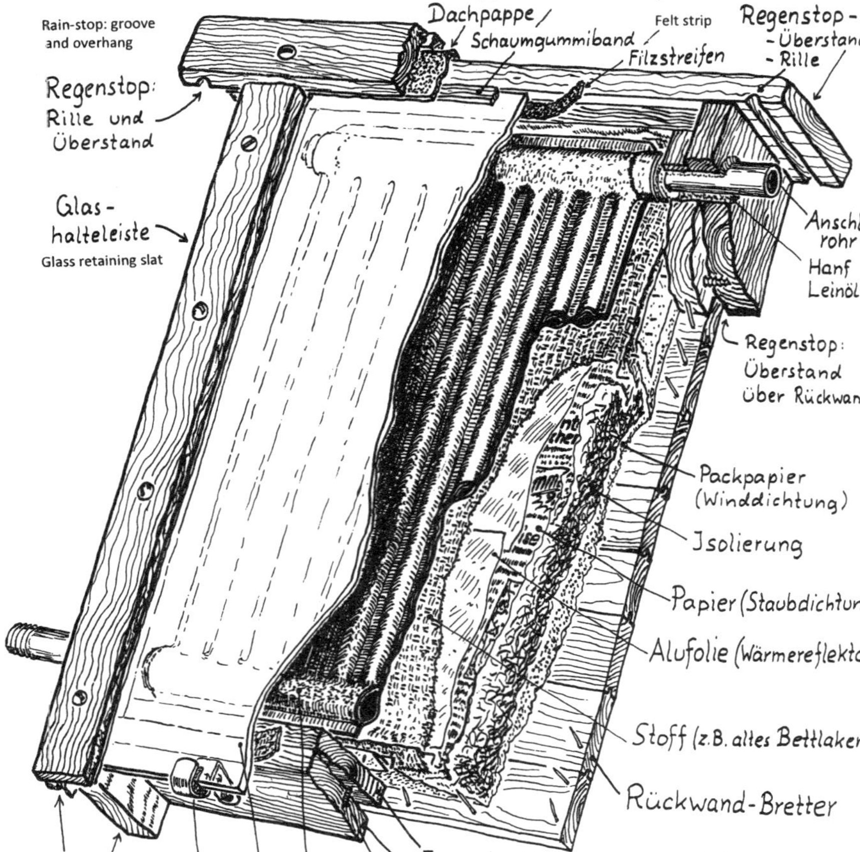

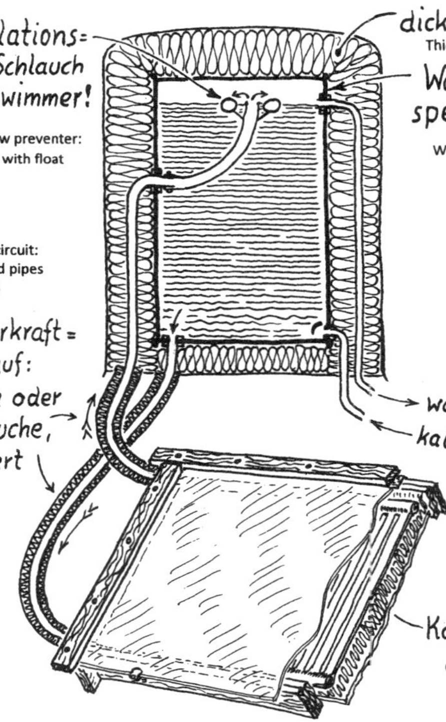

Einfachste komplette Warmwasser=Anlage: *Direkte Brauchwasser-Erwärmung, Speicher höher stehend als der Kollektor ermög=licht Schwerkraftumlauf, Rücklaufsperre macht Technik überflüssig. Mit Wärmetauscher (z.B. „Faß in Faß" auch für Winterbetrieb und hohen Druck.*

The simplest complete hot water system: Direct domestic hot water heating. Tank positioned above the collector enables gravity-fed system. The back-flow preventer eliminates the need for complcated technology. Heat exchanger (e.g. tank-in-tank) enables winter operation and high pressure.

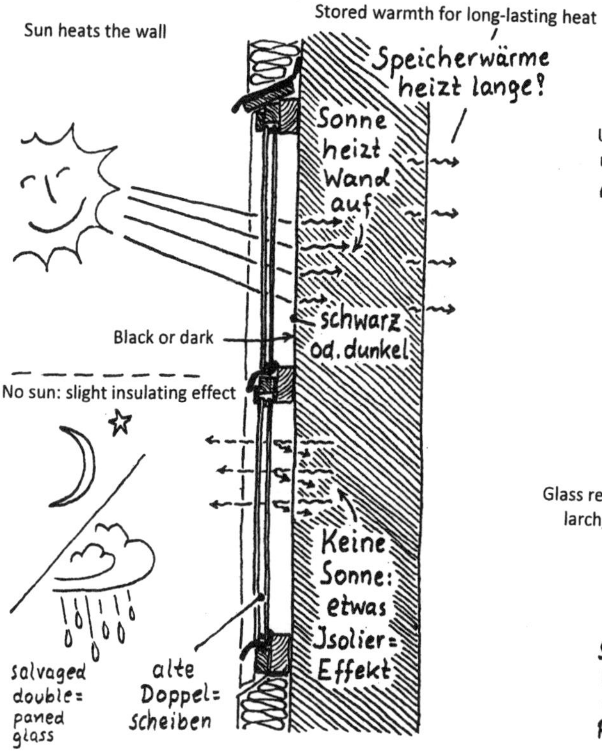

Solar-Heizwand.

Effekt ↗ und Details ↙

Solar heating wall. Effect and details

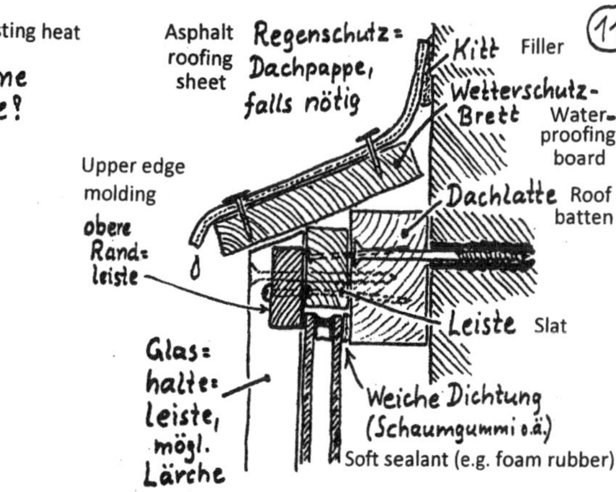

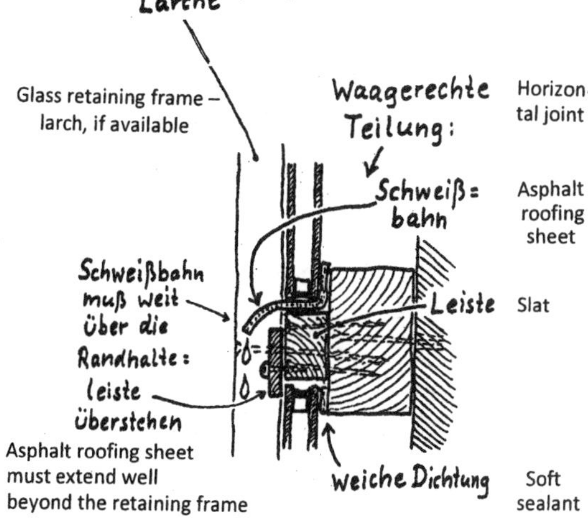

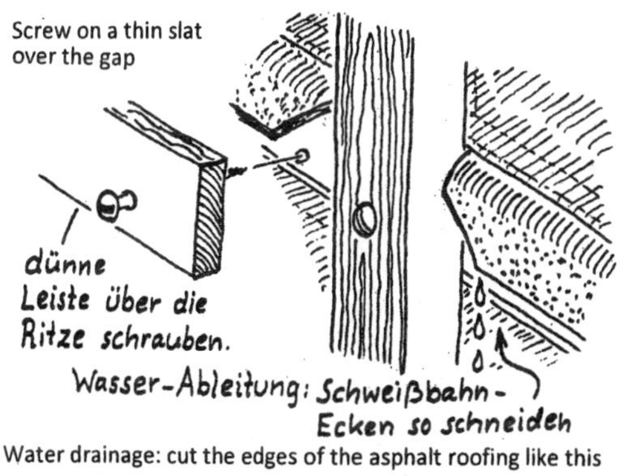

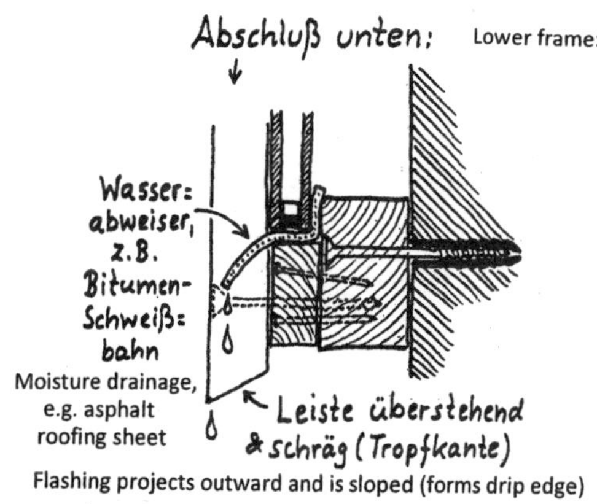

Eine Heizwand aus Altglas verkürzt die Heizperiode um etliche Wochen! Wozu teure Wärmepumpen usw, die uns bloß abhängig halten, wenn es doch so einfach geht... Eine Süd-Wand aus Massiv-Stein oder (Stroh-)Lehm, auf die im Winter kaum Schatten fällt, heizt erheblich mit, wenn Du sie verglast. Die Wand muß mindestens ziegelrot oder dunkel-lehmbraun sein, am effektivsten schwarz (Abtönfarbe, kein Teeranstrich!).

A heating wall made of salvaged glass reduces the annual heating period by weeks! Why buy expensive heat pumps, etc., which only increase our dependency when it's so simple... A **south** facing wall made of solid stone or adobe that gets direct sunshine in winter can make a major contribution to heating if you glass it in. the wall has to be at least brick red or a **dark** earth tone. Black is most effective (paint pigment, not tar coating!)

DAS ↑ ist die Wahrheit trotz grünmelierter Politik: Für eine Fabrik-Kollektoranlage von zB 4 m^2 darf man erstmal 5.000 Euro hinlegen, dann gibt's schlappe 500 Euro "Förderung". Selbstbauer kriegen gar nix, offenbar interessiert es nicht, daß Sonnenenergie genutzt wird, sondern man will viel Geld in gewisse Taschen pumpen. Darum: Jetzt erst recht! Wir bauen genau so starke Anlagen aus Schrott für 100 Euro, da dürfen sich die Herren mal 20 Jahre lang am Heißwasser die Finger verbrennen...

AUFRUF: Wer ein "Sonnenwärme-Nutzungs-Werk" gebaut hat, schreibe mir, wer beim Bau nicht weiterkommt, ebenso. Ich werde versuchen, Kontakte zur gegenseitigen Hilfe zu vermitteln. Bitte Rückporto beilegen.

Christian Kuhtz, Selbstverlag "Einfälle statt Abfälle", Hagebuttenstrasse 23, D-24113 Kiel (auch Bezugsquelle für die Bauanleitungen).

THAT ⇑ is the reality despite greenwashing policies: For a 4 m^2 factory-made collector system, for instance, you first have to shell out 5ooo €, and then you get a paltry 5oo euro "incentive" payment. For self-builds, you get nada. Obviously, it doesn't matter whether you use solar energy; the point is to channel lots of money into certain people's pockets. All the more reason to build a solar thermal system out of junk for 1oo euros that is just as good as an off-the-shelf system. The good gentlemen can scald their fingers for 2o years on our hot water...

APPEAL: Anybody who has built a "solar thermal energy system", please write to me, and also if you are building one and you get stuck. I will attempt to connect you with people who can help. Please enclose stamps.

Christian Kuhtz, "Einfälle statt Abfälle", Address see page 12.

⑭ Muß das sein ??? Is this really necessary ?

100% energy.... 1/3 power + 2/3 lost.... transmission losses.... transformer losses..... GREAT! There's still 25% left!

Du kannst auch ganz ohne Strom, ohne Kohle, nur mit Holz sehr komfortabel, sauber und effektiv heizen...

You can also get comfortable, clean and effective heat using wood alone, without using any electricity or coal at all...

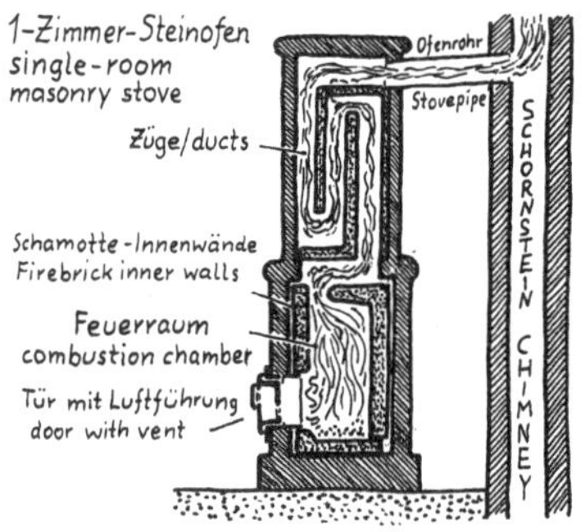

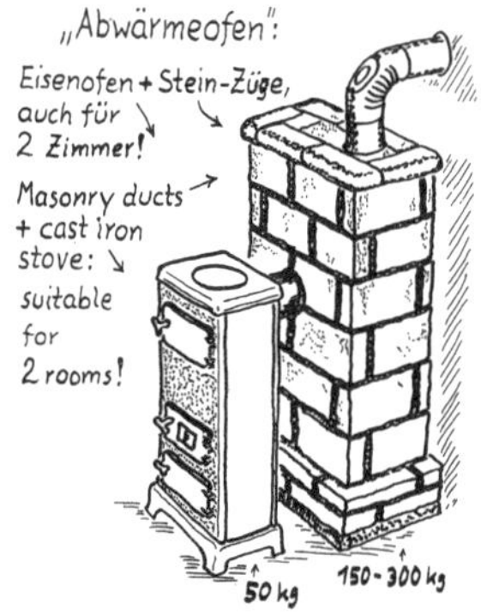

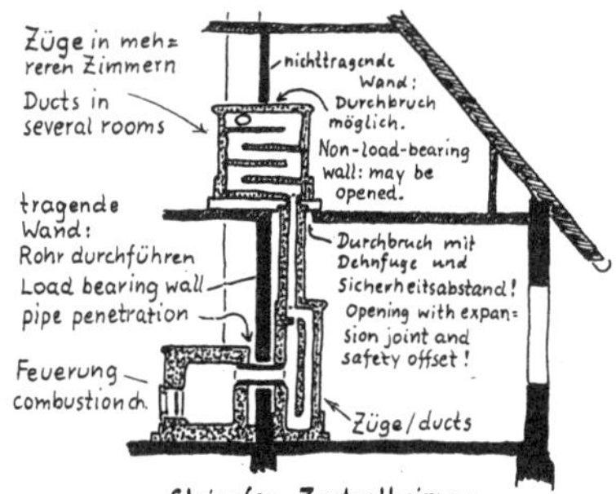

Steinofen-Zentralheizung
Masonry stove central heating

...im selbst gemauerten Steinofen! Einfachste Möglichkeit: „Abwärmeofen"!

Gute, einfache Bauart (Schnitt) →

...with your own home-made masonry stove! Simplest option: „Radiant heat" stove!

Simple and good design (section) →

Im vorhandenen Eisenofen nie mehr mit Kohle heizen, sondern: Nur ½-1 Std. mit Holz heizen gibt schnelle Wärme und vom Abwärmeofen bis zu 12 Stunden in den Ziegeln gespeicherte Dauerwärme. Die Feuerung (Eisenofen) hast Du schon, baust also nur noch die Züge! Ziegel, Lehmmörtel, evtl. innen Lehmputz-Auskleidung.

Never again use coal in your cast iron stove. Instead, heat with wood for ½-1 hour to provide fast heating and up to 12 hours of stored heat in the brick radiator. You already have the combustion chamber (cast iron stove). All you need now is the ducts! Bricks, loam mortar, and, if necessary, an internal clay plaster lining.

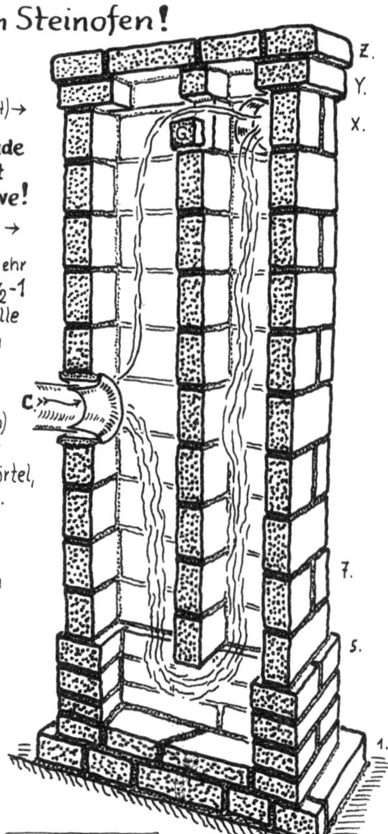

Ofen-Heft 5.

drittletzte Lage (X.)/Third-to-last course (X.):

In der Trennwand eine Lücke als Gasschlitz (G.), noch besser eine Anheizklappe. A hole in the divider wall serves as a gas slot (G.), – a warm-up flap is even better.

7. Lage/course (9., 11.,....): Der erste Zug (links) wird weiter als der zweite (rechts). The first duct (left) is wider than the second (right).

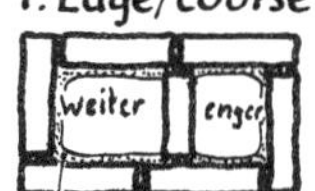

Optional liner -- clay/crushed brick mixture.
Auskleidung? Lehm-Ziegelsplitt-Mischung.

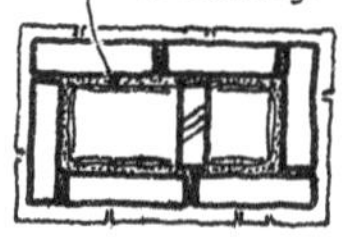

6. Lage/course: (8., 10., ...)

Der 3/4 Stein als Trennwand zwischen den Zügen steht auf dem Vorsprung von der 5. Lage. – Ankerdrähte einlegen! –

The 3/4 brick divider wall between the two ducts rests lip of the 5th course of bricks. Install anchor cables!

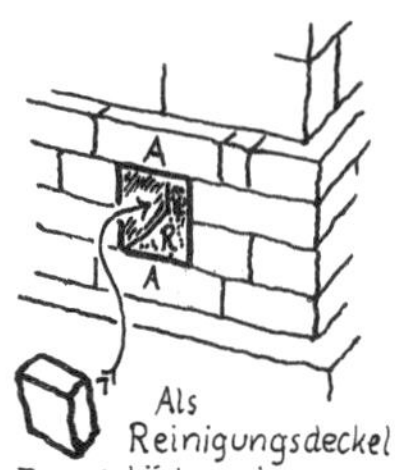

Als Reinigungsdeckel ½ Ziegel lösbar einmauern. Removeable ½ brick covers the cleaning opening.

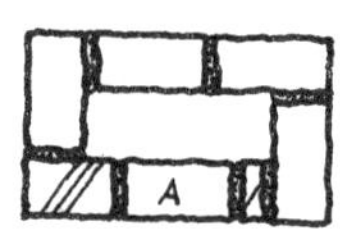

5. Lage: Stein A überbrückt die Reinigungsöffnung. **5th course:** Brick A bridges the cleaning opening.

Leichtester hoher Steinofen
Smallest masonry stove

Maße/dimensions 38×56 cm, Sockel/base 49×75 cm
Höhe/height 1,55 m, mit Sockel/with base 1,70 m.
Gut für 1 Zimmer/good for 1 room 16–25 m².
Speicherdauer / heat storage for 7–10 Stunden/hrs,
meist 2 × tägl. heizen je nach Kälte und Dämmung,
usually 2 × daily operation depending on temperature and insulation.

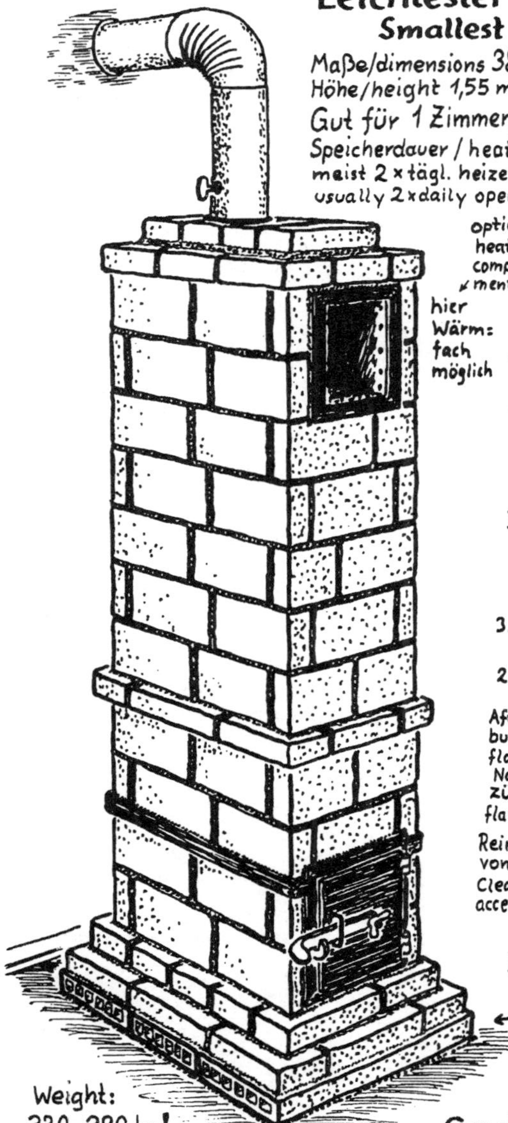

Weight: 330...380 kg!

Zu bauen aus
Built from:

- ~ 110 Dünnformat-Ziegeln (Roman bricks)
- wenigen Schamotteplatten (a few fireclay plates)
- Lehmputz-Auskleidung (clay plaster liner)

Dehnfuge/ Expansion joint = „D."

Zug = Duct

Ofenbau-Heft 3.

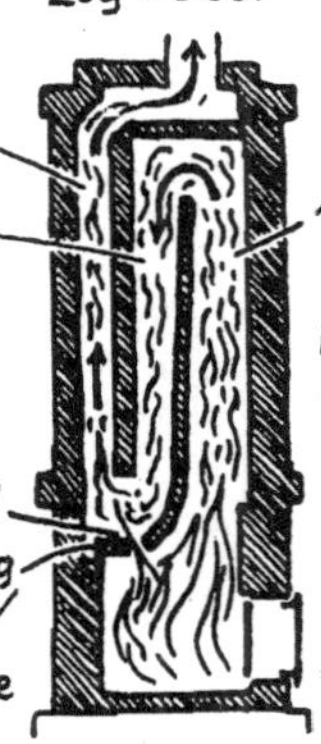

Zelltonplatten geben Unterlüftung und verhindern Wärmeabgabe in den Untergrund. Hollow clay bricks provide airflow from below and prevent heat transmission downward.

Gewicht 330...380 kg!

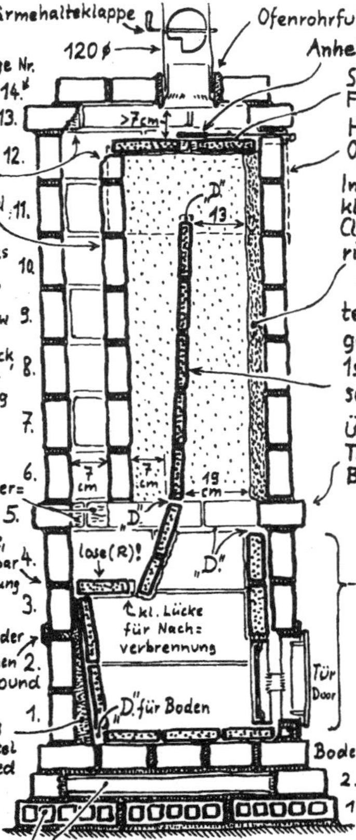

1st + 2nd brick course, firebox inside (top view):

1.+2. Hochkant - Ziegellage, darin Feuerraum:

First lay the bricks marked (x), then install door frame/ iron perime= ter, then fit in the remai= ning bricks.

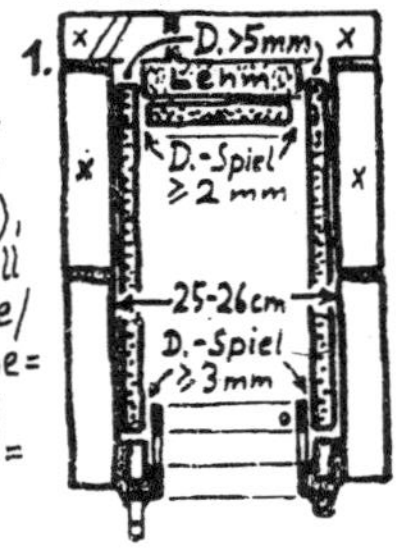

Erst die mit „x" bezeichneten Ziegel setzen, dann Türrahmen mit umlaufendem Eisen= rahmen draufmauern, dann die übrigen Ziegel einpassen!

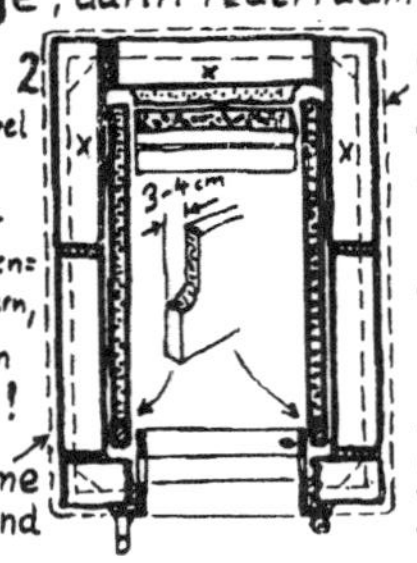

Zentralheiz-Steinofen. Beispiel, Teile des Systems „nebeneinander" gezeichnet:

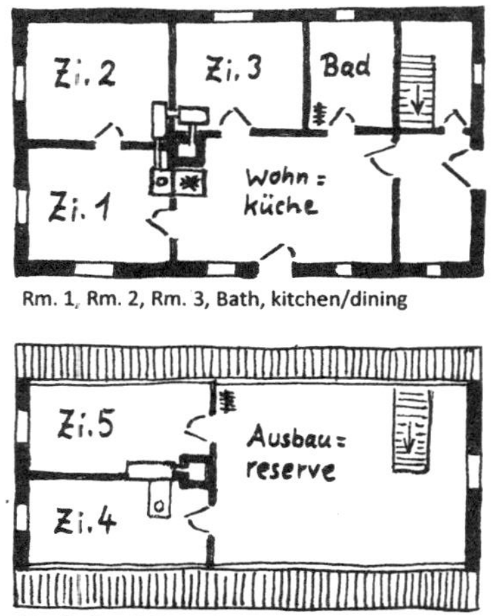

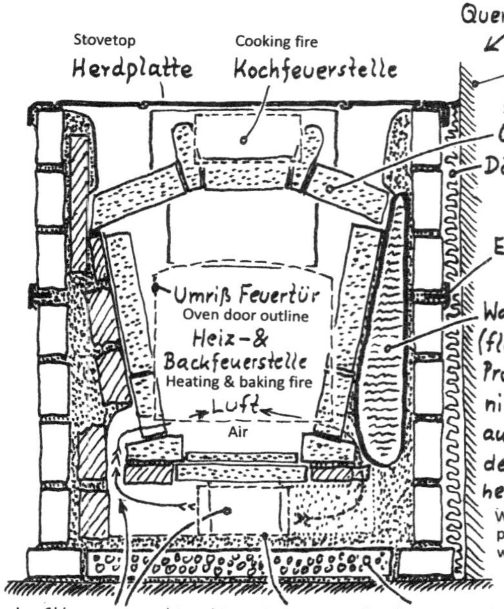

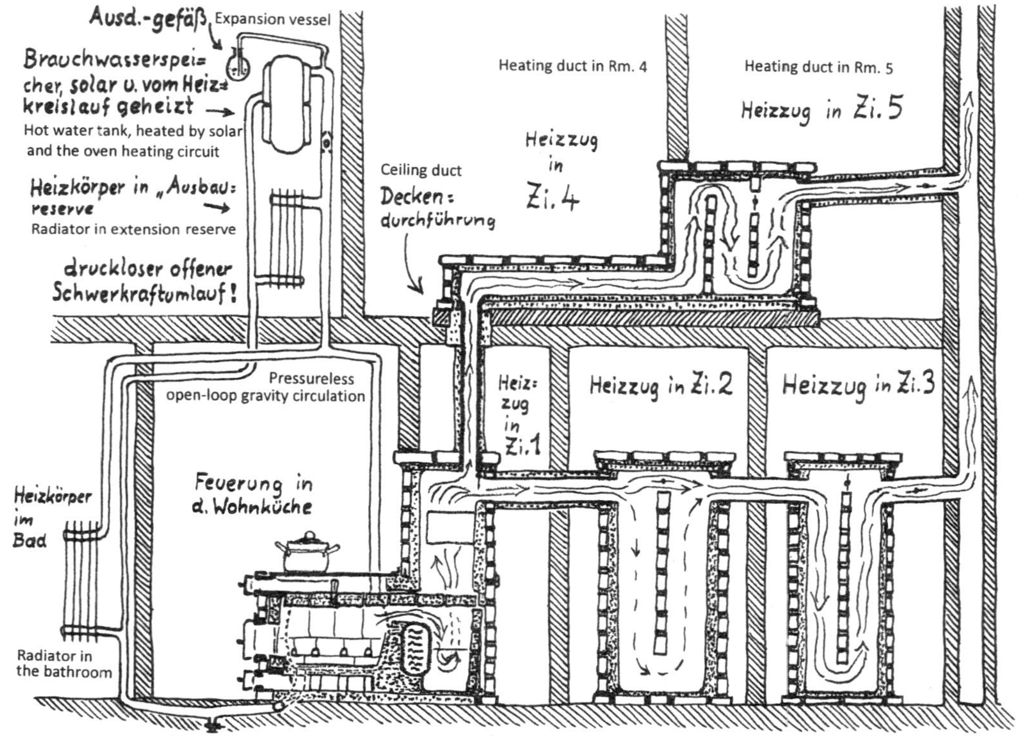

- Ziegel, außen — Bricks, external
- Ziegel- od. Plattenrest — Salvaged bricks or masonry
- Schamotte — Fire brick
- Lehmmörtel, Lehmputz — Clay mortar, clay plaster

Nicht nur ein Zimmer, auch das ganze Haus läßt sich unabhängig von Strom und Technik nur mit Holz komfortabel heizen!

Massiv aus Ziegeln & Lehm gemauerte Züge heizen 6 Räume in 2 Etagen direkt, weitere Räume & Warmwasser per Heizwasser-Schwerkraftumlauf, von 1 Feuerstelle aus. Zeitbrand: 1-2 Stunden Holzfeuer heiß und sauber abbrennend, dann Ofentür zu, gibt 24 Std. Dauerwärme. Wirkungsgrad gemessen 91 %.

Wood can be used to heat more than just a single room; the whole house can be heated comfortably without electricity or any other appliance! From a single source of combustion, massively built ducts made of brick and earth can directly heat six rooms on two floors, while additional rooms & hot water are heated via the gravity-fed hot water circuit. Intermittent firing: 1-2 hours of hot, clean-burning wood fire, then close the stove door and you'll have 24 hrs. of constant heat. Efficiency measured 91%.

Extrablatt

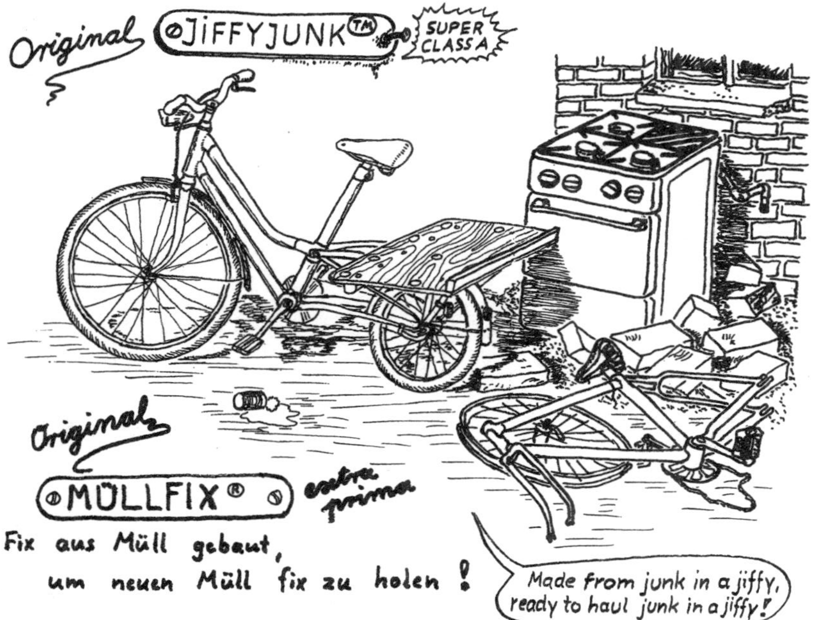

Aus einem miesen Schrott-Damenfahrrad wird ein Lastrad mit großer Ladefläche über einem Klapprad-Hinterrad. Hinterrad & Klimbim abbauen, Hinterradstreben durchsägen, kleines Hinterrad einbauen, Hinterradgabel so weit runterbiegen, daß das Tretlager wieder so weit überm Boden ist wie vorher, Hinterradstreben zur Sattelrohrmuffe biegen, passend hämmern & Schraube durch! Jetzt aus Sperrmüllholz und alten Zeltstangen den Gepäckträger bauen – fertig!

A defunct women's bike is transformed into a hauling bike with a big flat-bed mounted over the rear wheel from a folding bike.

Schuhe nähen • shoe-making

Vom gewünschten Schuh den Zuschnitt mit wasserlöslichem Filzstift auf den Fuß zeichnen.

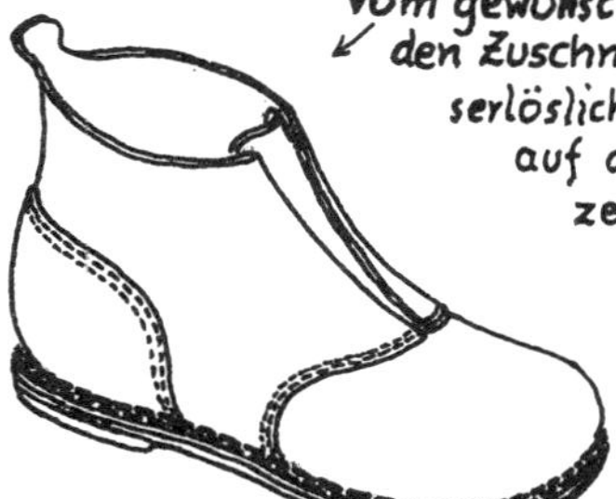

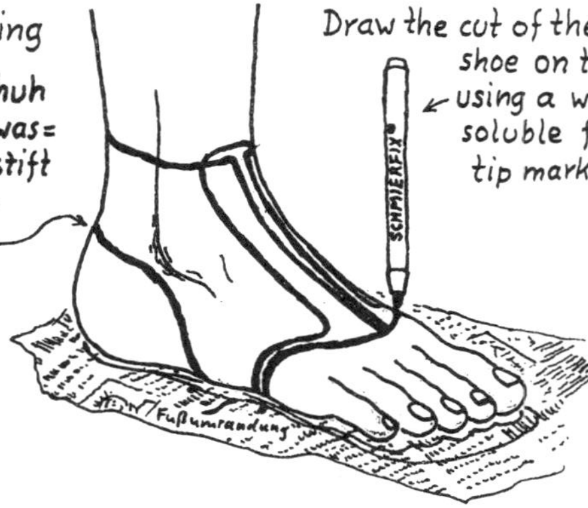

Draw the cut of the desired shoe on the foot, using a water-soluble felt tip marker.

Wichtige Hilfslinie: die Mittellinie. Hier jedoch keine Naht nähen (drückt oft)! Important guideline: the centerline – **but don't put a seam here, often it would rub!**

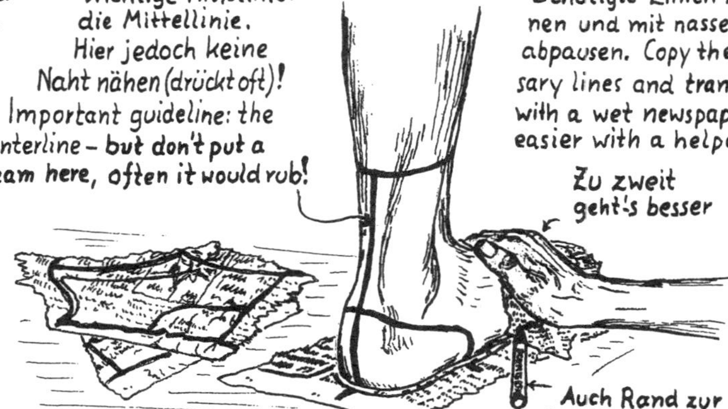

Benötigte Linien nachzeichnen und mit nasser Zeitung abpausen. Copy the necessary lines and transfer them with a wet newspaper – it's easier with a helper.

Zu zweit geht's besser

Auch Rand zur Sohle anzeichnen. Trace the outline of the sole as well.

Nach den Zeitungs-Abdrücken schneide Pappschablonen, und nach denen das Leder zu. Kanten abschrägen = „schärfen", aber nicht die Sohlen-Nahtzugabe (SNZ)! Nahtlinien anzeichnen, vorstechen, übertragen:
Use the newspaper transfers to cut out the cardboard patterns and then the leather pieces. Taper, or „sharpen" the edges, but not the ones of the sole-seam allowance (SSA)! Pencil-in and pre-punch the seams:

When sewn as cut out: – Ouch! The seam rubs. Always trim the rough side.

Wie geschnitten vernäht: drückt! Darum immer die rauhe Seite abschärfen.

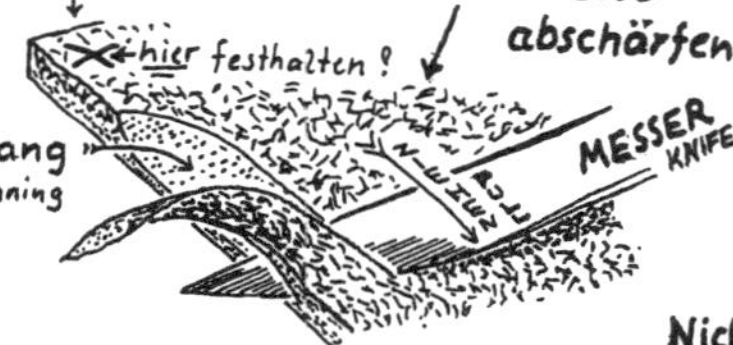

Trick: Spitze gleitet auf Glasscheibe!
Trick: knife tip glides on glass!

Nichts von der glatten, haltbaren „Narbenseite" abschneiden!
Don't trim the smooth, durable side!

Good Gut:

inneres Leder nur bis zur 2. Naht abschärfen. Trim inner layer of leather only to the 2nd seam.

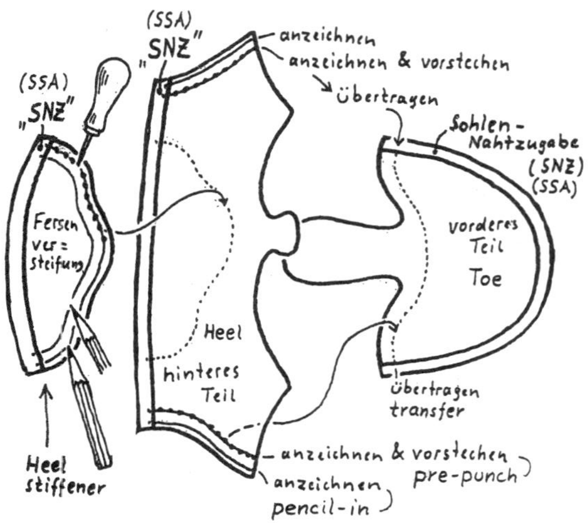

Sew the leather upper. Good & not much work: 2 parallel saddle-stitched seams with doubled thread using a leather needle. Ripples the leather somewhat so that the stitching is sunken to protect against abrasion. Oberleder nähen: Gut & wenig Arbeit: 2 Sattlernähte parallel mit je 1 doppeltem Faden mit Schwertnadel. Kräuselt das Leder etwas, Stiche liegen versenkt →

gegen Abscheuern geschützt.

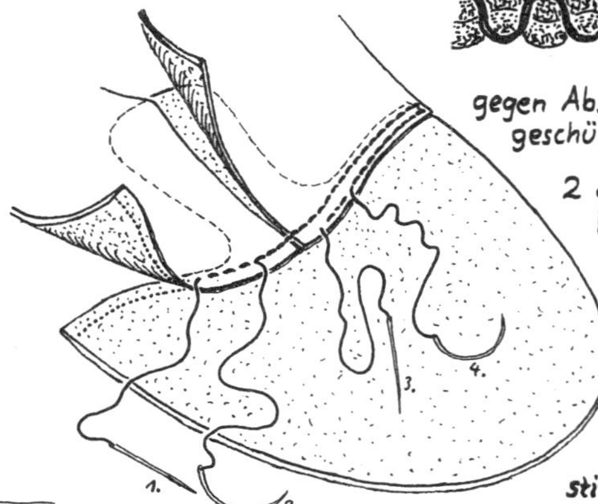

2 doppelte Heftstichnähte machen mehr Mühe...
2 double saddle-stitched seams require more effort.

Extrablatt

So kommt die Sohle dran:
Here's how the sole is attached:

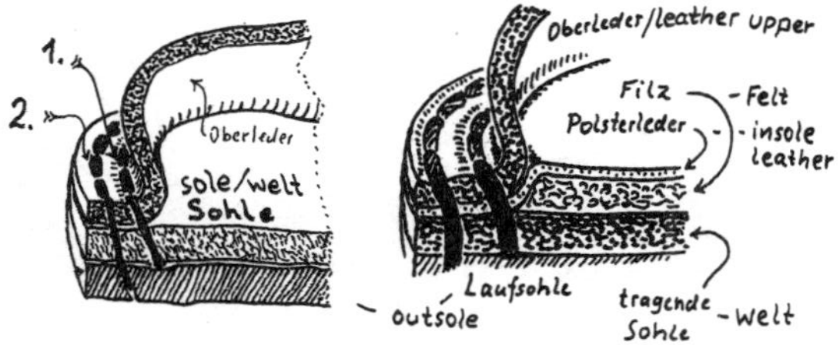

1. Naht spannt das Oberleder um den Leisten. Erst mit der 2. Naht hält's auf Dauer, dabei Laufsohle mit festnähen oder später ankleben. **Beste Paßform & warme Füße gibt ein mit eingenähtes Polsterleder + Filz drunter!**
1. Seam stretches the leather upper over the last. 2nd seam ensures durability; sew on the outsole with the 2nd seam, too, or glue it on later. A sewn insole with felt underneath ensures the best fit and warmest shoe.

Oberleder wässern (macht es formbar)/Moisten the leather upper thoroughly (makes it pliable)!...

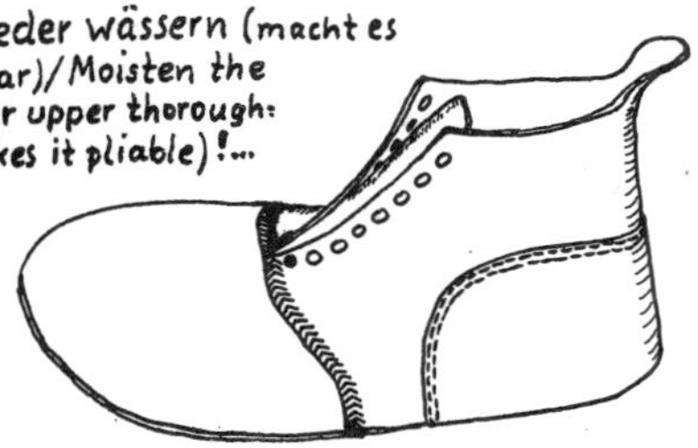

... an den Sohlenrand heften und sofort ringsum festnähen! ... tack it to the edge of the sole and sew it on immediately!

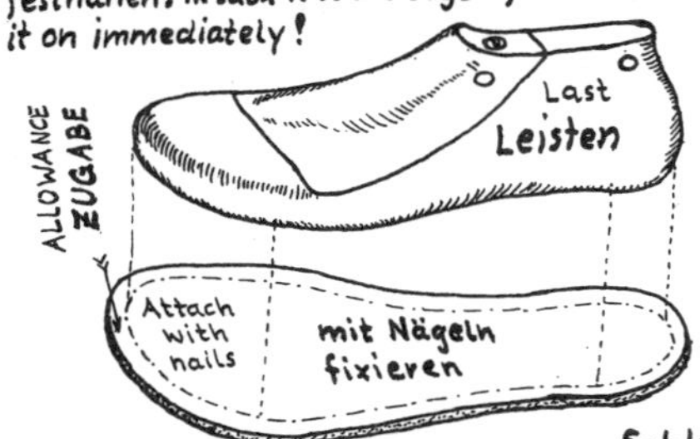

Sohle, doppelt so dick wie das Oberleder.
Sole, twice as thick as the leather upper.

Um den Leisten spannen:
Stretch over the last:

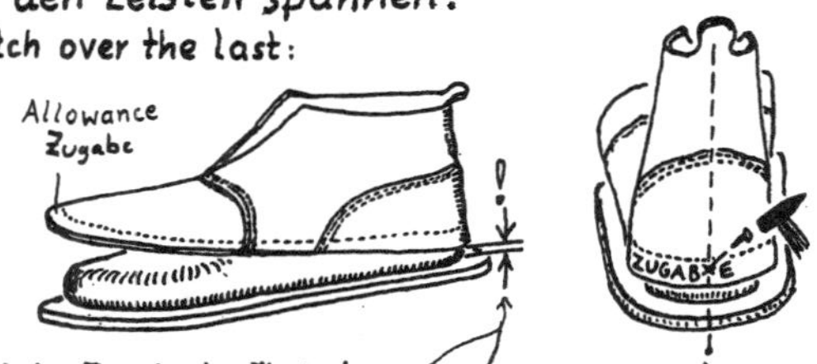

Rand der Zugabe berührt eben die Sohle. Mittellinie Hinterteil auf Mittellinie Leisten, 1 Hilfsnagel halb einschlagen. Dann Leder strammziehen & mit Täcksen (Heftnägel) anheften:

The edge of the allowance aligned evenly with the sole. Centerline of the heel aligned w. centerline of the last. Pound nail in halfway, then pull the leather taut and tack it into place with shoe nails:

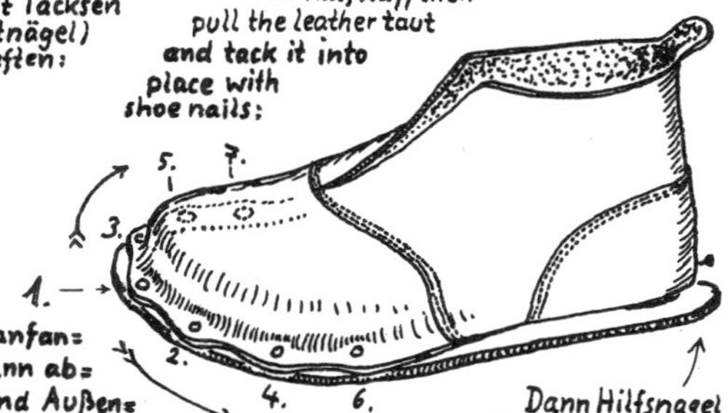

Vorne anfangen, dann abwechselnd Außenseite (2,4,6) - Innenseite (3,5,7) weiter nach hinten.
Begin in front, then alternate between the outside (2,4,6) and the outside (3,5,7) moving backward.

Dann Hilfsnagel raus, Seiten- und Fersenbereich heften. **Then remove the alignment nail and tack on the sides and the heel.**

Heften: How to tack:

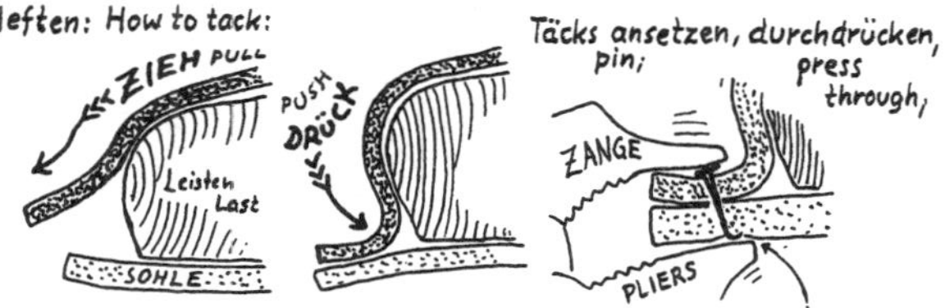

Spitze trifft die andere Zangenbacke und krampt sich um. Tip of nail strikes the opposite jaw of the pliers bending back on itself.

! Sohlenrand zum Nähen anfeuchten, die ganze 1. Naht nähen, so lange das Oberleder noch naß ist. Moisten the allowance of the sole, sew the entire 1st seam while the leather upper is still wet.

Richtig vorstechen / Pre-punch it right:

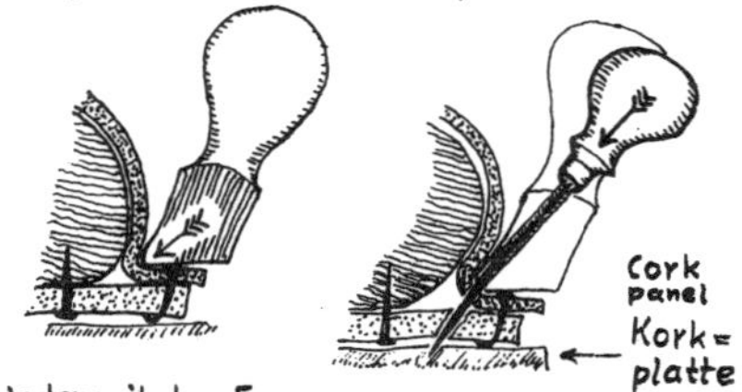

Oberleder mit dem Formholz kräftig in die Kerbe zwischen Leisten und Sohle drücken, direkt neben dem Formholz genau im Winkel vorstechen. Firmly push the leather upper into the notch between the last and the sole; pre-punch precisely into the formed angle.

Nähen: mit „Pechdraht". Anfang: Pechdraht bis zur Mitte durchziehen. Sewing with **waxed thread**. Beginning: Pull the thread through to the middle.

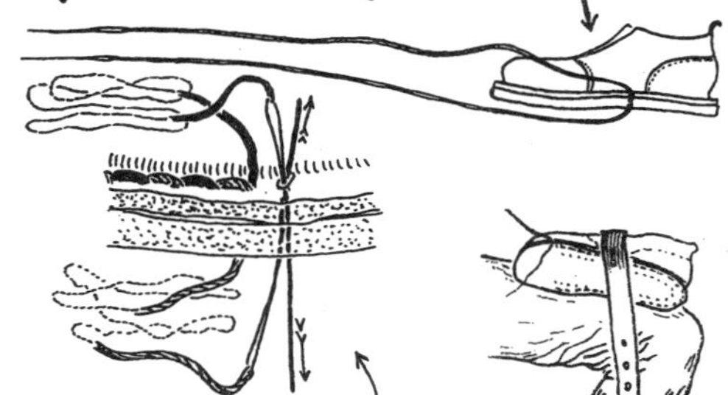

Loch vorstechen. Drähte gegeneinander durchschieben, **Fäden** durchziehen und beide zugleich kräftig strammziehen. Pre-punch the hole. Push the wires through **in opposite directions**. Pull the thread through and **firmly pull both ends** taught simultaneously.

Spannriemen: „Dritte Hand" beim Sohlennähen! Belt as „third hand" when sewing soles!

Immer die Heftnägel entfernen!
Always remove the shoe nails!

Haferflocken aus der TÜTE?

NEE DANKE! vielleicht 'n andermal! Tschüß...

Store-bought rolled oats? NO THANKS!

Maybe some other time – see ya...

Bau' Dir Deine eigene Müsli-Quetsche!

Build your own grain flaking mill!

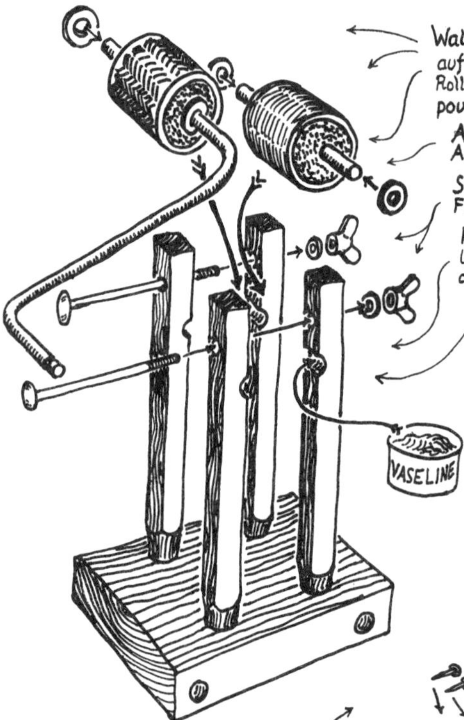

Walzen: 2"-Heizungsrohr. Oberfläche riffelig meißeln & überfeilen, auf gedrechselten Holzkern treiben oder mit gutem Beton vollstampfen. Rollers: 2"-heating pipes. Ridge the surface with a chisel and file, pound onto turned wooden cores or fill with good compacted concrete.

Achsen mittig, Rundeisen 12 mm Ø. Axles well-centered, 12 mm Ø steel rod.

Spannschrauben zum Einstellen des Preßdrucks (grobe oder feine Flocken). Bolts & wing nuts to set tension (rough or fine flakes).

Hartholzleisten (von Sperrmüll-Möbeln) federn und gleichen Ungenauigkeiten aus. Hardwood posts (from salvaged furniture) damper and compensate for irregularities.

Achsen laufen prima in gefettetem Holz. Axles move great in greased wood.

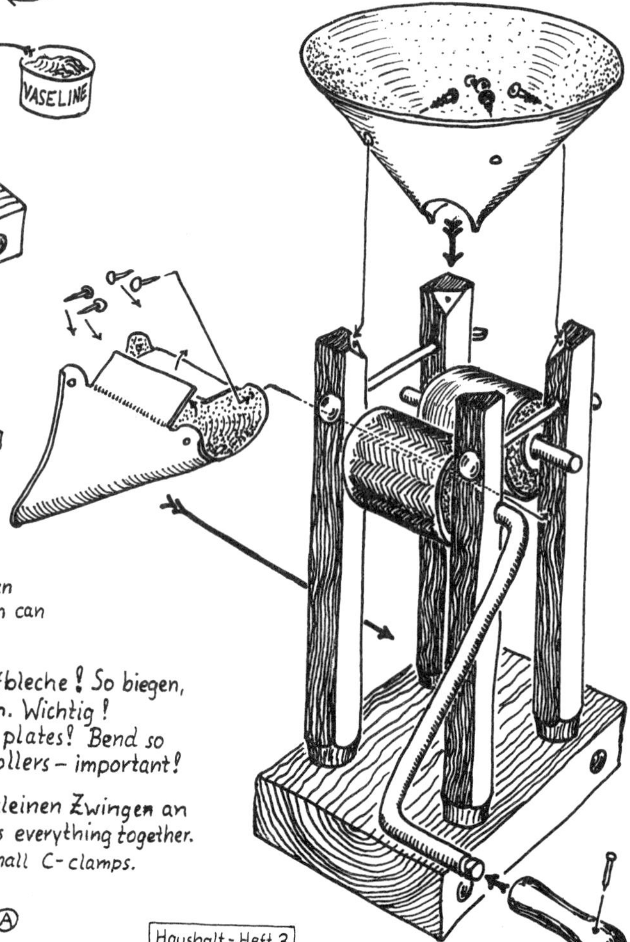

Trichter aus Dosenblech bördeln, Mündung mit möglichst kleinem Spalt zu den Walzen zuschneiden. Shape funnel from a tin can; cut the bottom slot to fit the rollers without leaving a gap.

Rutsche aus Dosenblech, führt die Flocken in die Müslischüssel. Tray made from a tin can guides the flakes into the cereal bowl.

Laschen oben an der Rutsche = Abstreifbleche! So biegen, daß sie die Flocken von den Walzen lösen. Wichtig! Flaps on the top of the tray = extractor plates! Bend so that they extract the flakes from the rollers – important!

Holzklotz hält alles zusammen. Mit 2 kleinen Zwingen an Tisch o.ä. festmachen. Wood block holds everything together. Fix the mill to the tabletop with two small C-clamps.

Vorratsmiete, nur gelegentlich zu öffnen. Wenn vorhanden, statt Laub auch Stroh / Strohballen praktisch.

Food storage pit, for occasional opening only. If available, use also straw and straw bales instead of foliage.

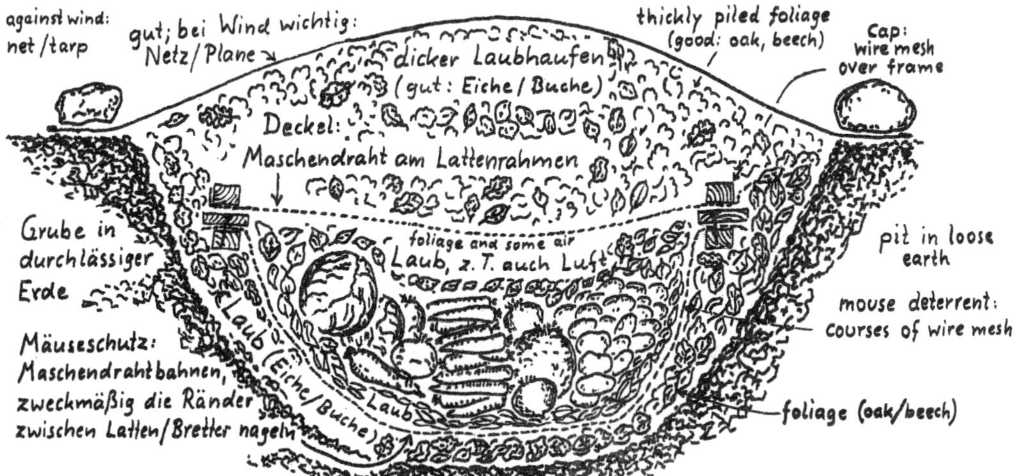

Extrablatt

Edel: Erdkeller aus Lehm-Matsch und Trümmersteinen mauern! Hilfsmittel: →

Luxury root cellar made from loam-mud and salvaged brick masonary! Tools: →

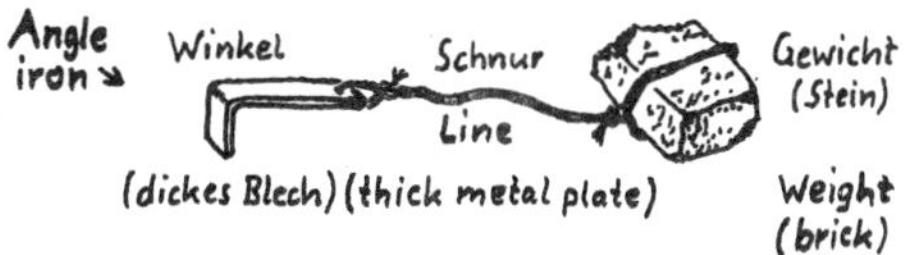

Reihenfolge / steps:

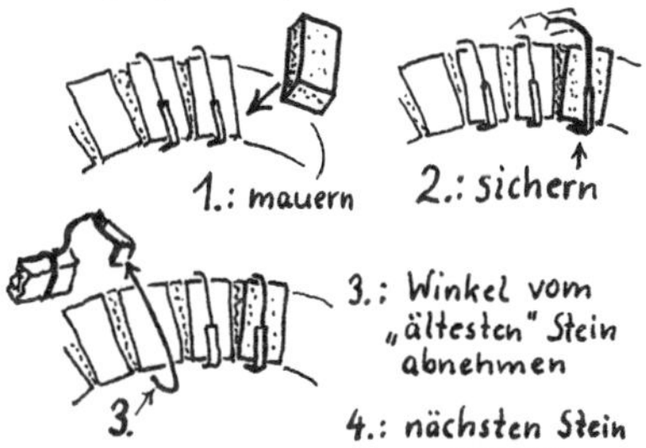

1.: lay brick 2.: secure 3.: take angle iron from the „oldest" brick laid 4.: lay next brick

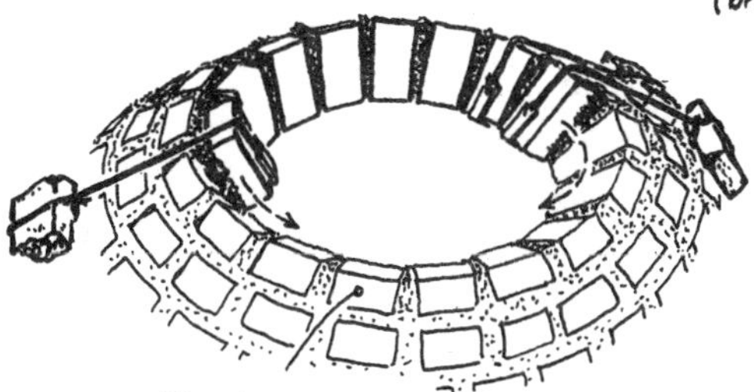

Ein schon fertiger Ring stützt sich selbst. Während des Bauens die letzten Steine mit solchen Haltewinkeln sichern, bis ein neuer Stein davorsitzt.

The completed ring of bricks supports itself. During construction, secure the most recently laid bricks with angle irons like these until you lay the next brick.

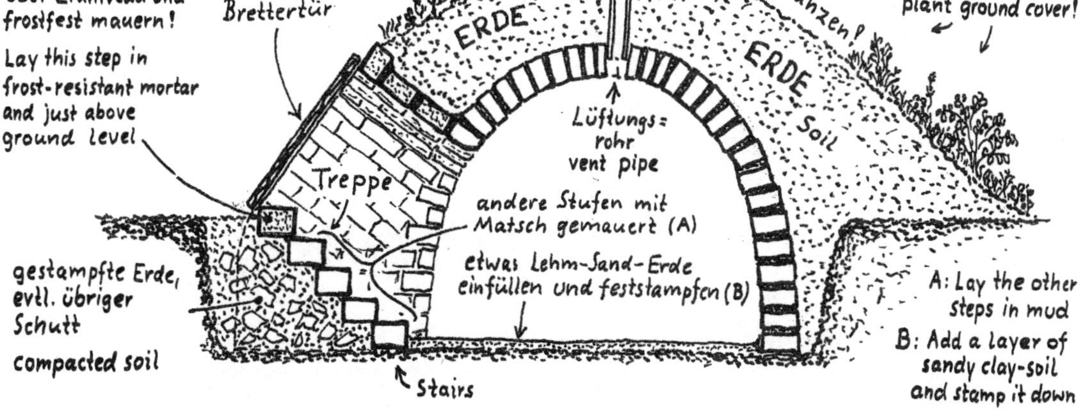

JA-DAS IST FORTSCHRITT, DER DIENT UNS ALLEN...

Jeden Tag essen wir von Pflanzen, die auf der Erde gewachsen sind, wir nehmen also von der Erde. Doch was geben wir ihr zurück? Das was von der Natur bestimmt war, als guter Dünger wieder zu Erde zu werden, damit neue Pflanzen wachsen können, lassen wir in den Kanälen der Wasserklotechnik verschwinden, weil es so "üblich" ist. Damit es in unseren Häusern auch fein aussieht, lassen wir noch Unmengen kostbares Trinkwasser hinterher rauschen (ca. ein Drittel des Wasserverbrauchs jedes Bundesbürgers rauscht durchs Klo).

Früher konnte noch der Klärschlamm aus dem Wasser gefiltert, abgelagert und - mit einigen Problemen - als Dünger verwendet werden, "nur" das Trinkwasser war verloren. Heute geht nicht einmal mehr das, das Abwasser enthält so viele Gifte aus Wasch- und Putzmitteln, Chemikalien, Öl, Benzin, Reifenabrieb, Schwermetalle und was sonst noch alles von den Straßen der Autogesellschaft geschwemmt wird, daß wir per Wasserklo aus Naturdünger und Trinkwasser unter riesigem technischen Aufwand eine Mischung entstehen lassen, die nur noch als Giftmüll "entsorgt" werden kann.

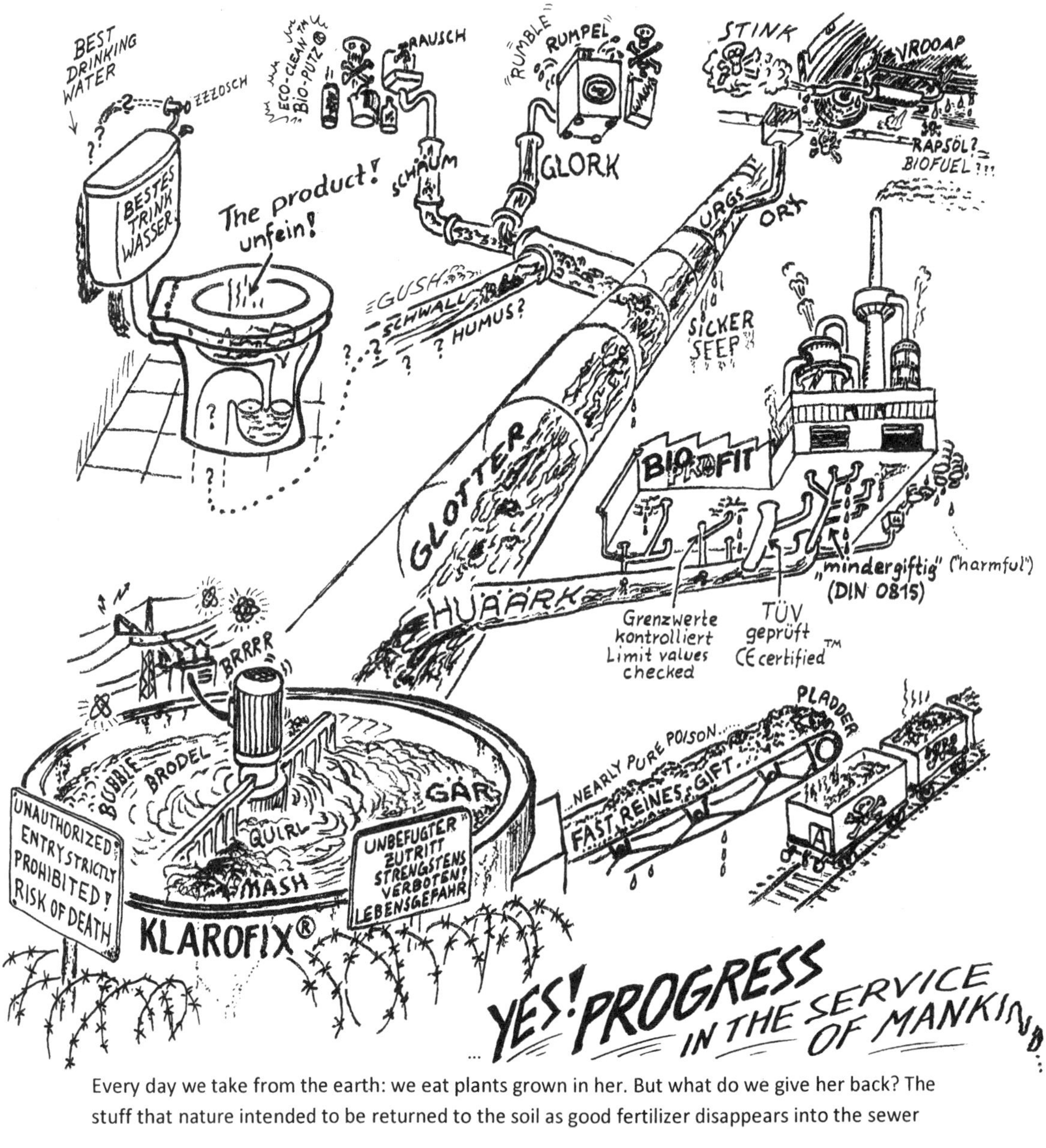

Every day we take from the earth: we eat plants grown in her. But what do we give her back? The stuff that nature intended to be returned to the soil as good fertilizer disappears into the sewer pipes of our flush toilets because, "that's the way it's done". To keep our houses sparkling clean we allow huge amounts of precious drinking water to go sloshing along behind it . . . It used to be that "only" the drinking water was lost. We used to be able to filter the sludge out of the water, store it, and—with a very great effort—use it as fertilizer. Today, even that isn't possible.

There is so much poison from detergents and cleaning agents, chemicals, oil, gasoline, tire residues, heavy metals, and who knows what else flooding the streets of our car-centered culture that all we can do with the natural fertilizer and drinking water from our flush toilets is create a mixture which is only suitable for "disposal"—with massive technological effort—as toxic waste.

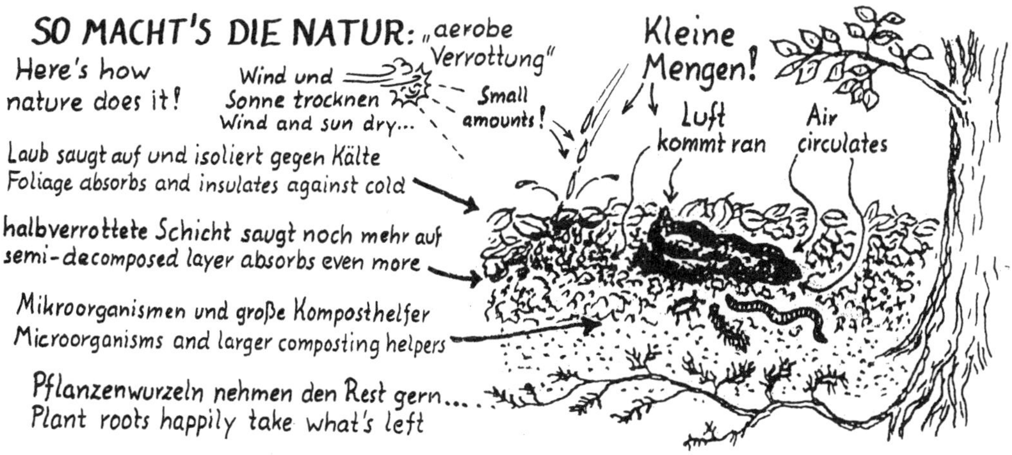

So bleibt für uns die eigentlich naheliegendste Möglichkeit: "Gucken wir doch ab, wie es die Natur machen will!" Ein Kackhaufen liegt auf lockerem Waldboden gut durchlüftet und vom Laub gegen Kälte geschützt, unzählige kleine Lebewesen verwandeln ihn sehr bald zu Humus. Das Flüssige von einem Mal Pinkeln wird vom Laub aufgesaugt und in der obersten Bodenschicht festgehalten, wo es ebenfalls schnell mit verrottenden Pflanzenteilen zu Humus wird. In einem echten Kompostklo geht es genauso:

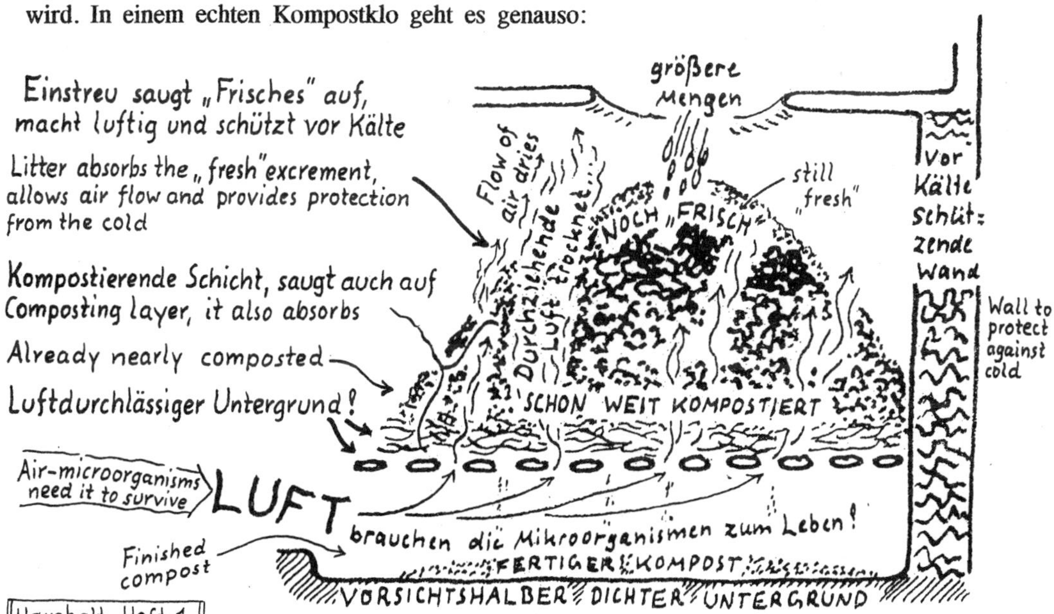

Haushalt-Heft 1.

But we have another, obvious alternative: look how nature does it! A pile of crap sits on the forest floor, well aerated and protected from the cold; innumerable small creatures transform it quickly into humus. The liquid from a pee is absorbed by foliage and captured in the uppermost soil layer where, along with biodegradable vegetation, it is also quickly converted to humus.

We can use this natural system for large quantities too: Here's how a real composting toilet works

„Der elektrische Wäschestampfer" The electric laundry tamper

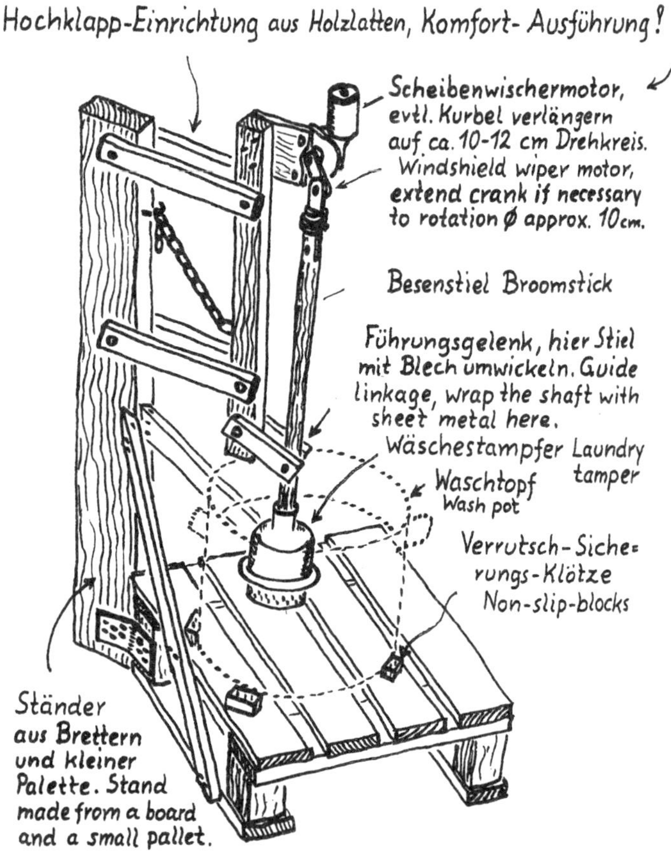

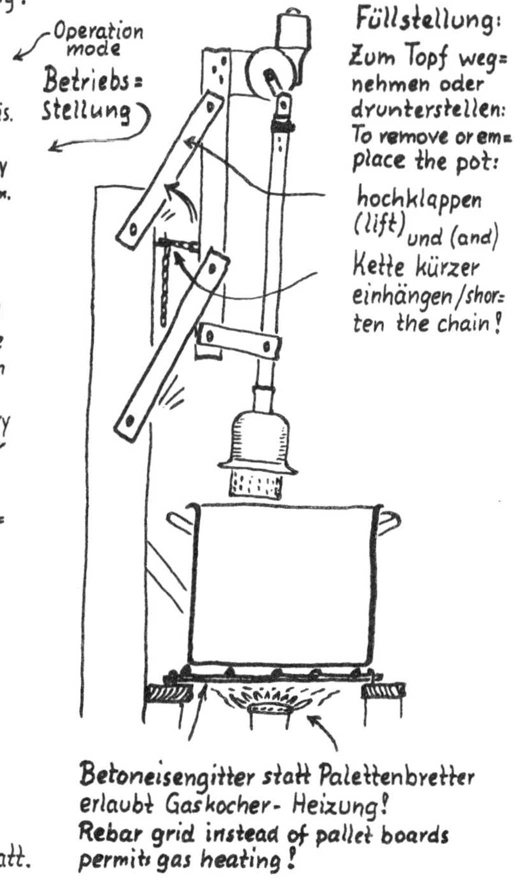

Stromverbrauch: 12 Volt, 25 Watt.

Bewegungsablauf / Range of motion:

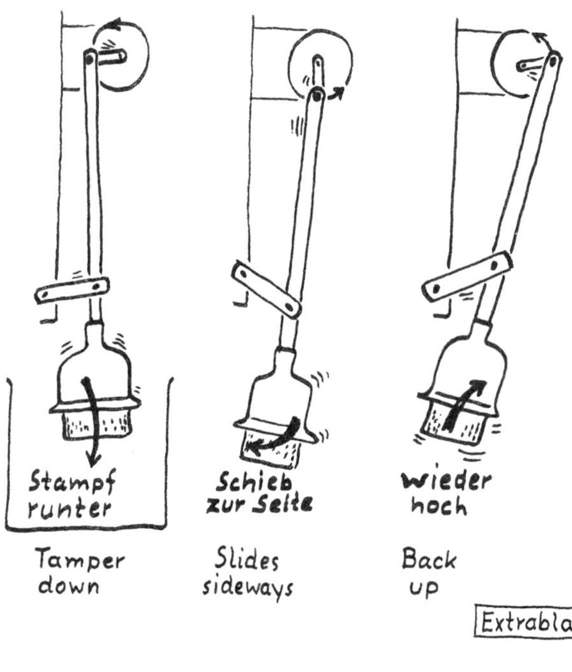

Der Stampfer stampft rauf-runter und bewegt sich auch seitlich. Wichtig, damit nicht immer nur eine Stelle der Wäsche gestampft wird.

Kette so einhängen, daß der Stampfer in oberster Kurbelstellung fast überm Waschwasser steht. Nur wenig Wasser nötig!

Überlastungsschutz: Ist zu viel Wäsche unterm Stampfer, hebt er sich selbst samt Hochklapp-Einrichtung ein Stück hoch.

The tamper pounds up and down and moves sideways, important to prevent tamper from repeatedly striking the laundry in the same spot.

Adjust the chain so that in the highest position, the tamper is almost out of the water. Only a little water is needed!

Overload protection: when there is too much laundry under the tamper, it lifts itself a little.

Power consumption: 12 Volts, 25 Watts.

„Altglas-Direktrecycling":

Aus Gläsern und Flaschen, die sonst bestenfalls im Container landen würden, entstehen ganz ohne Fabrik und Schmelzofen neue nützliche Dinge wie Trinkbecher, Schüsseln, Untersetzer, Kerzenständer, Trichter, Laternen und vieles mehr: Bindfaden schneidet das Glas zu!

Old glass -- direct recycling:

From jars and bottles, which would otherwise end up in the dumpster at best, new and useful things can be created without any factories or smelting furnaces – things like cups, bowls, coasters, candle holders, funnels, lanterns, and much more. Twine cuts the glass to size!

Beispiele: Examples:

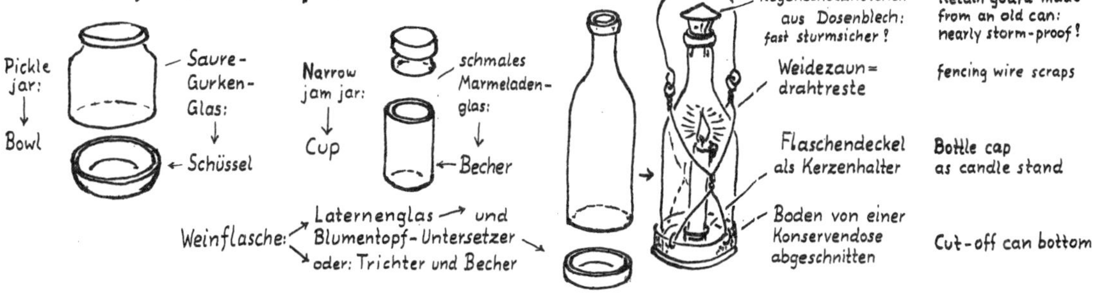

Wine bottle → funnel and cup, or: flower pot saucer and lantern

Einfachste „Glaswerkstatt": Zu zweit werken. Zwei Astgabeln fest in die Erde schlagen, Flasche drauflegen, gut festhalten und so „sägen":

Extrablatt

Simplest „glass factory": two people work together. Pound two forked sticks firmly into ground, place bottle on top, hold on tight and „saw" like this:

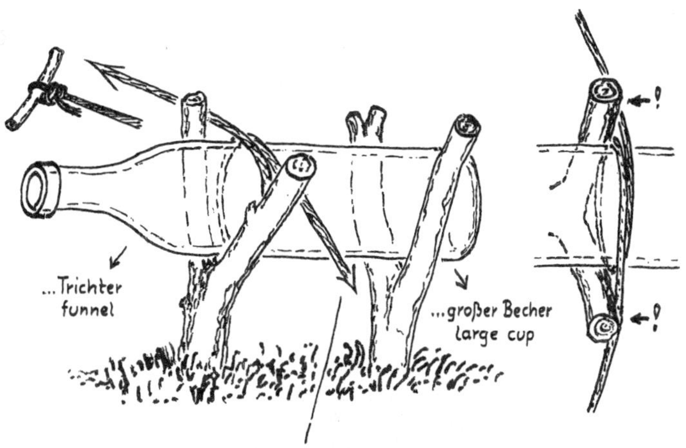

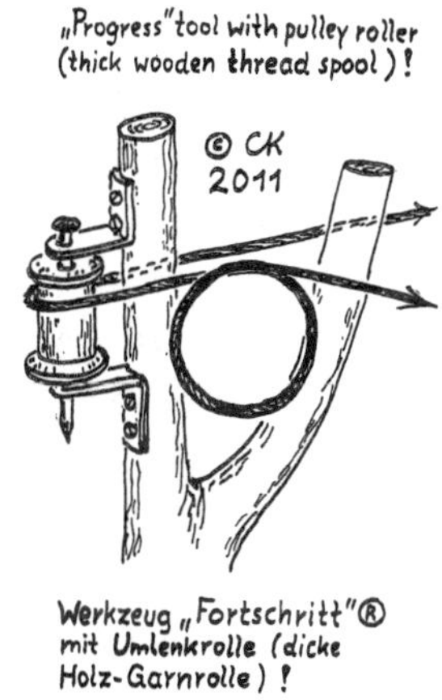

Dicken Hanfbindfaden 1x drumwickeln und unter strammer Spannung schnell hin- und her ziehen.

Dabei leicht an einer der Astgabeln entlangziehen als Führungshilfe.

Die führende Astgabel genau quer zur Flasche ausrichten, damit die Enden der Schlinge aneinander liegen:

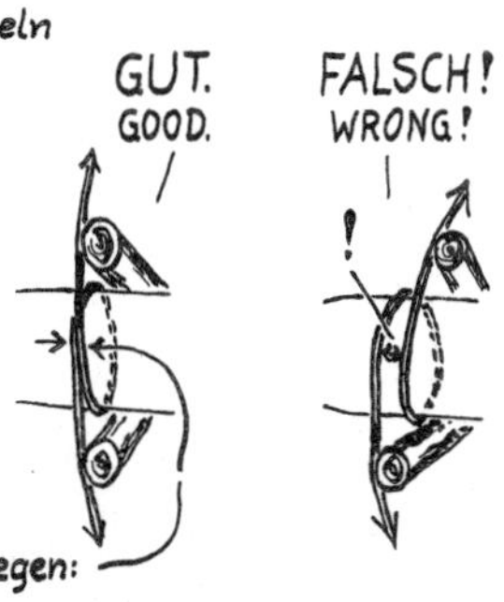

Wrap the hemp twine 1x around, pull back and forth quickly under constant strong tension.

Use one of the forked branches as a guide.

Make sure the forked branch is at an exact right angle to the bottle so that the ends of the loop are snug against one another.

Die Reibungshitze sprengt die Flasche (und kohlt den Bindfaden an). Bruchkanten mit feinem Sandpapier entschärfen. Reißt der Faden, bevor die Flasche springt, oder lassen Eure Kräfte zu früh nach, die Flasche blitzschnell in kaltes Wasser tauchen! Neuer Versuch? Erst wenn die Flasche wieder kalt und trocken ist.

The heat generated by friction cracks the glass (and burns the twine). Sand the broken edges smooth with fine sand paper. If the twine breaks before the glass cracks, or if you tire out too soon, dunk the glass into cold water immediately! Need to try again? Wait until the glass is cold and dry.

(26) Die fahrende Töpferwerkstatt...

Töpferbrand unterwegs im „Einmal-Brennofen" aus 2 10-Liter-Blechdosen (Fritierfett=dosen, Gurkeneimer o.ä. von Gastwirtschaften), Dachziegelresten o.ä. als Brennraumboden, einem mitgebrachten Ofenrohr (1 m lang, ca. 12 cm ∅), Erde zum Wärmehalten drüber.

Fire pottery on the go in a „single-use kiln" made of two 10-liter tin cans (from deepfryer grease, pickles, or similar cans from restaurants), discarded roof tiles (or the like) for the firing chamber floor, a stovepipe (1 m long, ~12 cm ∅), covered in soil to keep in the heat.

Aufbau:

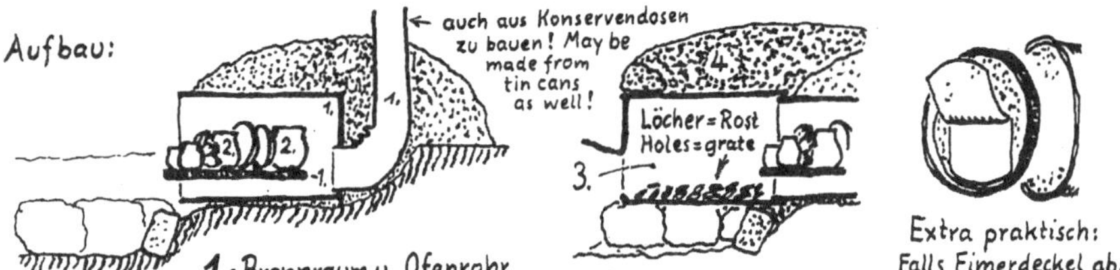

1.: Brennraum u. Ofenrohr fertig, Erde drüber, damit alles fest steht, Brennraumboden rein. / Assemble firing chamber and stovepipe, cover with soil to hold everything in place, insert the firing chamber floor.
2.: Tonarbeiten rein / Put the pottery inside.

3.: Feuerraum dran / Attach combustion chamber.
4.: Erde drüber / cover with soil.
Tip: Eimerhenkel als Schür=haken! Use handle of can as a fire poker!

Extra praktisch: Falls Eimerdeckel ab=nehmbar, daraus die Feuertür bauen! If lid of can is removeable, make it into the kiln door!

Ein Töpferbrand dauert lange und ist sehr spannend. Du mußt min=destens 3 Stunden heizen und wenigstens über Nacht abkühlen lassen.

Im Blechofen aus 2 10-Liter-Eimern kannst Du 1 Schuhkarton proppevoll mit Tonarbeiten bei 1000 °C brennen und brauchst dafür ca. 1½ Apfelsinen=kisten voll trockenem Reisig. Wenn es beim Brand irgendeine Schwierigkeit gibt, brauchst Du sofort mehr Holz, lege deshalb lieber doppelt so viel bereit. Du hast nur zu Anfang des Brandes noch Gelegenheit, Dich um Holz zu kümmern. Später mußt Du fast pausenlos nachlegen, sonst sinkt die Temperatur sofort wieder!

Die Tonarbeiten müssen gut getrocknet sein!

Heize den Brand unbedingt sehr langsam und vorsichtig an! Wenn etwas zerspringt, dann fast immer zu Anfang des Brandes: Plötzliche Hitze läßt „gebundenes Wasser" verdampfen, die Arbeiten werden vom Dampf gesprengt.

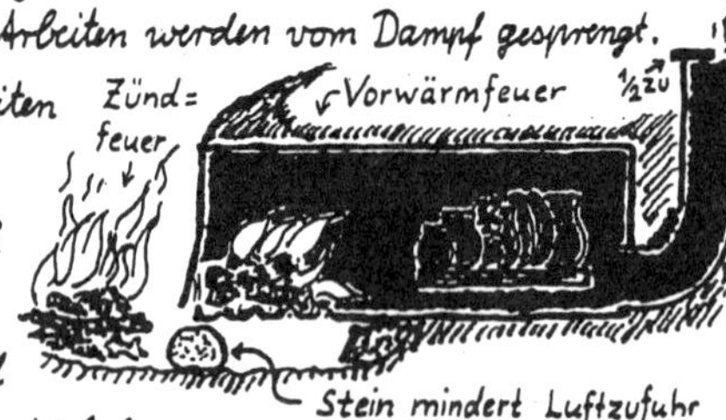

Die Flammenspitzen dürfen die Arbeiten höchstens ganz kurz, am besten nie, berühren! Daher zünde nie mit viel Papier oder Spänen im Ofen, sondern mache vorm Ofen ein Feuerchen und lege 2-3 dickere, kurze brennende Holzstückchen davon nahe der Feuertür in den Ofen. Mit einem „Lockfeuer" im Ofenrohr findet der Rauch schnell den Ausgang, obwohl der unten ist.

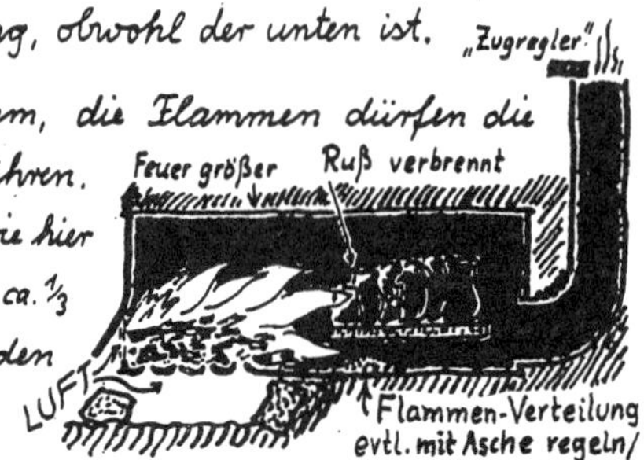

Nach ½ Std. steigere das Feuer langsam, die Flammen dürfen die Arbeiten jetzt immer öfter etwas berühren. Wenn Du beim einfachen Blechofen (wie hier gezeichnet) beobachtest, daß mehr als ca. ⅓ der Flammen unter den Brennraumboden ziehen, bleiben die Arbeiten zu kalt. Schiebe dann Asche unter den Brennraum.

Nach einiger Zeit (½ Stunde) erkennst Du, daß der Ruß an den Arbeiten zu verbrennen beginnt, die Farbe des Tones wird wieder sichtbar.

The mobile pottery studio

Firing pottery takes a long time and is very exciting. You have to heat the kiln for at least three hours and allow it to cool at least overnight. In a tin kiln made of 2, 10-liter cans you can fire a shoebox full of pottery at 1000°C. You'll need approx. 1 1/2 orange crates full of dry brushwood. If there are problems during firing, you'll need more wood right away, which is why you should collect twice as much as you need. The only opportunity you'll have to get wood is at the before firing. Later, you'll have to constantly stoke the fire; otherwise the temperature will drop off immediately! Make sure the pottery has is very dry. Take care to heat up the kiln very slowly and carefully. Cracking almost always happens at the beginning of firing. Sudden heat causes trapped water to vaporize, causing the pottery to crack. Initially, the tips of the flame should not —or only briefly— come into contact with the pottery. You should therefore not use a lot of paper or wood shavings in the kiln. Instead, build a pilot fire in front of the kiln and push 2-3 somewhat thick, fast-burning pieces of wood from the pilot fire through the fire door into the kiln. Light a small fire in the stovepipe to draw the smoke out of the kiln. After half an hour slowly stoke up the fire. It's okay for the flames to come in contact with the pottery more frequently at this point. In a simple tin kiln (like the one shown here), if you notice that more than about 1/3 of the flame is underneath the firing chamber floor, it means that the pottery is not hot enough. Push some ashes underneath the firing chamber. After a while (1/2 hour), you'll see that the soot on the pottery will begin to burn, the color of the clay will again become visible.
The most delicate part of the firing is complete!

Soon, cold air entering through the fire door can potentially do more harm than excessive heat. Keep the fire door wide open when stoking the fire but always close it just enough to prevent black, sooty smoke. That gives the fire just enough air for good firing while preventing too much cold air from getting into the kiln.

Die heikelste Etappe des Brandes ist geschafft! Bald schadet kalte Zugluft durch die Feuerluke mehr als zu kräftiges Heizen. Steigere das Feuer bei ganz offener Luftzufuhr, aber schließe die Feuerluke nach dem Nachlegen stets so weit, daß es gerade noch nicht rußt. Dann kriegt das Feuer so viel Luft, wie es für gute Verbrennung braucht, ohne daß viel überschüssige kalte Luft sich in den Ofen mischt. So gibt es die größte Hitze. Nach ca. 1 Stunde beginnen die Arbeiten zu glühen (650°) - das erste „Erfolgserlebnis"!

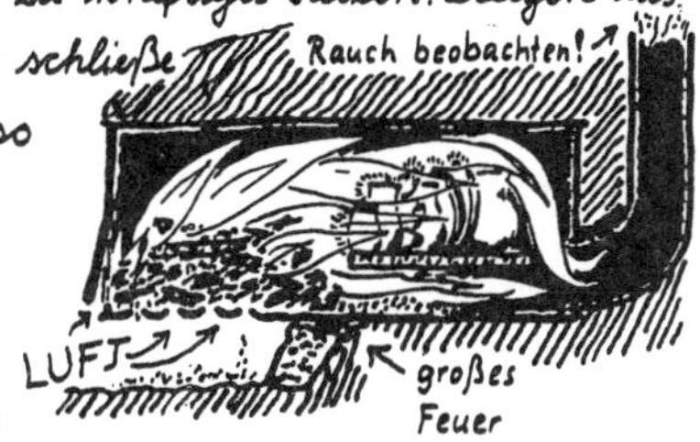

Ab jetzt steigere das Feuer, wie Du nur kannst. Liegengebliebene Glut stört, wenn sie zum Berg wird. Darum nimm nur dünnstes Holz, nicht über kleinfingerdick. Halte die Luftzufuhr frei! Lege lieber öfter kleine Portionen nach, sonst muß zu viel Holz auf einmal zünden, so daß das Feuer für kurze Zeit im eigenen Rauch erstickt und qualmt statt heizt. Schließe die Feuertür, so weit wie es ohne Rußen geht (s.o.) und achte darauf, daß der Durchgang unterm Brennraum nicht ganz verstopft. Inzwischen bullert es abenteuerlich im Ofen, das Rohr beginnt zu glühen und oben lodert vom Feuer rot erleuchteter Rauch heraus. Die Feuerluke speit unerträgliche Hitze, gegen die ein zweites Blech schützt.

Trotzdem heize weiter „was das Zeug hält". Bald glühen die Arbeiten hellrot (800°), hellorange (900°) und schlüßlich schon mit gelblich leuchtenden Rändern (1000°). Nur wenn das Holz gerade abgebrannt ist, kannst Du die Glutfarbe einen Augenblick lang sehen, dann mußt Du schon schnellstens nachlegen, damit die Temperatur nicht zu sehr absackt, und die Flammen versperren wieder jede Sicht. Hast Du zum letzten Mal nachgelegt, warte, bis die Flammen nachlassen, dann vermindere den Zug Schritt für Schritt so, daß das Holz ohne unnötig kühlende Luftzufuhr abbrennt und verglüht: Feuerluke zu, Ofenrohr 3/4 zu, Luftzufuhr immer weiter zu, dabei durch eine Ritze der Feuerluke das Feuer beobachten. Sonst kann es Risse durch „Kaltluft-Schock" geben! Ist kaum noch Glut da, verschütte Feuerloch und Luftzufuhr mit trockener Erde und decke das Ofenrohr ganz zu.

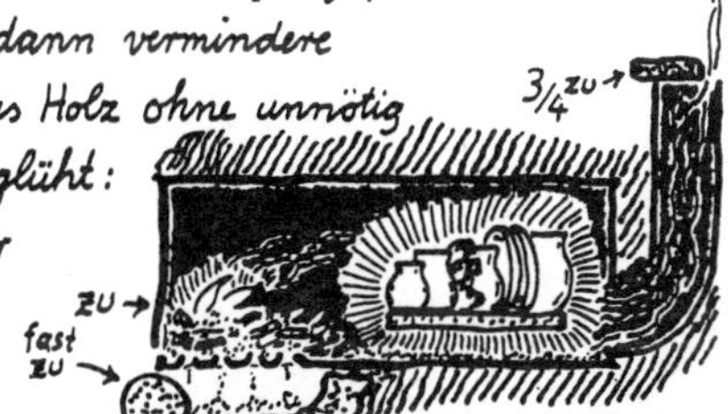

Die Arbeiten sollen bis zum Morgen langsam abkühlen. Bevor Du sie herausnimmst, öffne zuerst das Ofenrohr und fühle, ob noch Hitze herauskommt. Dann warte noch mit dem Öffnen des Ofens, bis nur noch ganz laue Wärme aus dem Rohr steigt, damit es nicht zum Schluß noch Kälterisse gibt. Und jetzt wird es ganz spannend... Handwerk-Heft 1.

That's how you get high heat. After about 1 hour the pottery will begin to glow (650° C)—the first taste of success!

From now on, stoke up the fire as much as possible. Embers get in the way if they're allowed to pile up. To prevent that, use very thin pieces of wood, no thicker than your pinky finger. Allow plenty of airflow! It's better to continuously add small portions of fuel to the fire; otherwise too much wood has to burn at one time, causing the fire to briefly smother itself in its own smoke, merely smoking instead of putting out heat. Open the fire door as far as possible without allowing the fire to smoke (see above) and make sure that the passage underneath the firing chamber does not get completely stopped up. Soon the fire will really start raging in the kiln. The pipe begins to glow, and smoke—blazing red from the fire—comes out from above. The fire door spits out unbearable heat which can be blocked with a second sheet of metal.

Keep on stoking the fire as hot as it will go. Soon the pottery will begin to glow bright red (800°C), bright orange (900° C), and finally with yellowish glowing edges (1000° C). You'll only be able to see the color of the glow for an instant right after the fire consumes the wood. Then you have to add more fuel as quickly as possible to prevent the temperature from dropping off too much, and then the flames will block your view again. The last time you add fuel, wait until the flames die down, and then reduce the airflow incrementally to allow the wood to burn and turn to embers while preventing unnecessary cooling from outside air. Close the fire door. Close the stovepipe ¾ of the way; continue to reduce airflow while keeping an eye on the fire through a slit in the fire door. Too much cold air getting into the kiln can result in "cold air shock" and cracked pottery. Once the embers have almost completely died down cover the fire hole and the air vent with dry soil and completely close the stovepipe.

The pottery should slowly cool down overnight. Before you remove it, first open the stovepipe and feel if heat is still coming out. Wait until only lukewarm air comes out of the pipe before opening the kiln, to prevent the cold from cracking the pottery at the very end. And now it gets exciting...

Für Kinder: Viele fleißige Hände kneten Bälle aus Lehm, Erde und Wasser, platschen sie zu einer Kuppel zusammen, und schon bald steht ein **echter BACKOFEN!**

For kids: industrious hands form balls of loam, soil, and water, patting them together to form a dome and before you know it, you've got a **real oven!**

Die einfachste Art: Vorher gemeinsam Lehm suchen und ein paar Tage einweichen. Dann: **1. Bau-Tag...**

The easy way: go out together and find some loam, let it soak for a couple of days. And then: **1st construction day...**

Ofen-Boden / Oven floor

Mixture: loam-water slurry and lots of dry sandy soil.

Mischung: Lehm-Wasser-Brei und viel trockene Sand-Erde.

„draufklatschen", glattklopfen, glattstreichen, antrocknen lassen.

pat down, top flat, smooth over, let dry.

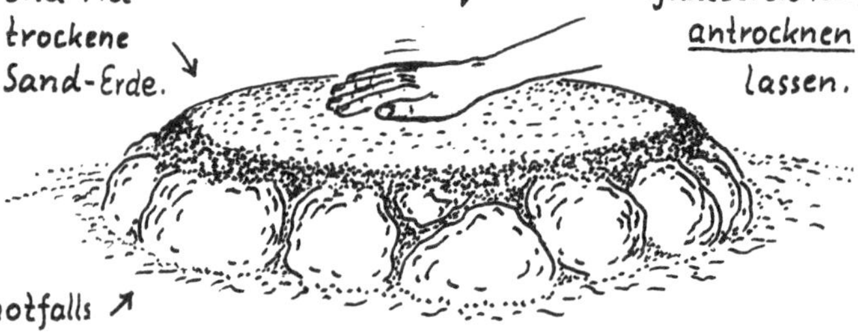

Sockel aus Steinen, notfalls gestampfter Erdhügel.

Base of stones. In a pinch, a compacted mound of earth will do.

Erhöht steht der Ofen im Trockenen!

An elevated oven is a dry oven!

2. Bau-Tag | 2nd construction day...: Viele feste **Lehmbälle** formen! Form lots of firm balls of loam!

Mixture like the one for the oven floor, but drier and with more sand.

Mischung wie beim Ofen-Boden, aber trockener und noch mehr Sand.

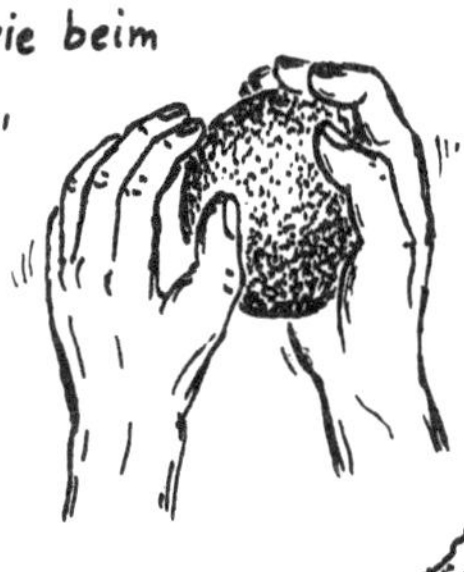

Von Hand zu Hand „platschen" macht glatt, fest und klebrig.

„Clapping" the balls from hand to hand makes them smooth, firm and sticky.

Auf Plane oder feuchte Lumpen legen, nicht auf Erde. Noch weich verbauen!

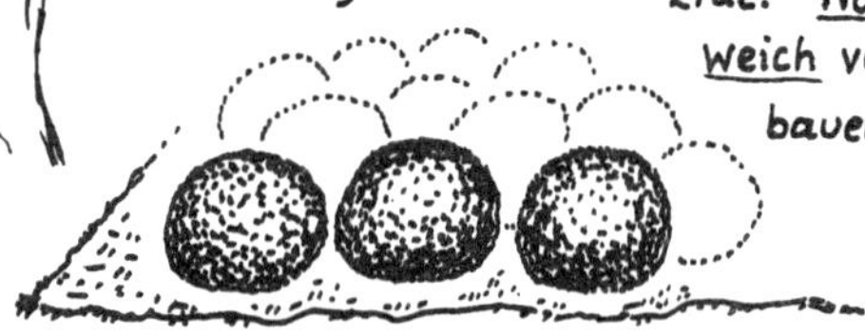

Lay the balls on damp rags, not on the ground. Build while they are still soft!

Support mold: / Stützform:

giant half egg made of wet sand. Pat it down well.

Halbes „Riesen-Ei" aus feuchtem Sand, gut festklopfen.

Brush any sand off the edge of the oven floor and cover it with a sticky layer of loam-slurry.

Sand vom Rand des Ofenbodens fegen und Lehmbrei als Klebschicht draufstreichen.

Gewölbe / dome

drumherum bauen:

Die Bälle stets an den vorigen Ball „dranplatschen", dann passen sie sich gut aneinander an.

Always „slap" the next ball onto the previous one, so that they fit together nicely.

Ball für Ball schließt sich das **Gewölbe** um das Sand-Ei:

Ofenbau-Heft 6.

Ball by ball the **dome** closes over the sand egg:

Bälle „platschen", aber:
Nicht ins Sand-Ei hineindrücken, keinen Sand zwischen die Bälle kommen lassen, klebt nicht. Notfalls mit Lehmbrei wieder klebrig machen.

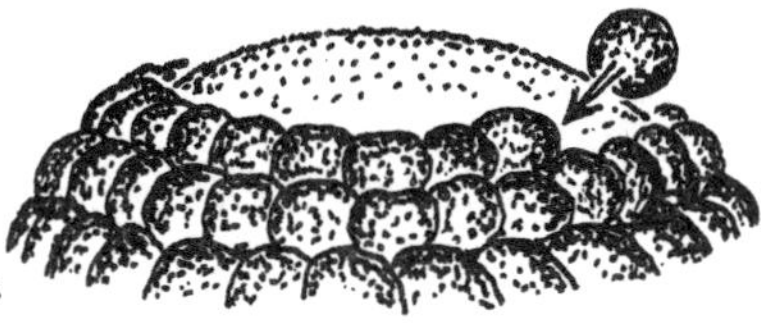

Trick: Zeitungspapier übers Sand-Ei legen!

„Slap" the balls, but do not press them into the sand egg and do **not allow** the sand **to get between the balls**, otherwise they will not stick together. Re-moisten the balls with loam-slurry if necessary. Trick: lay newspaper over the sand egg!

With open hands, pat down the finished dome...

...and let dry!

Fertiges Gewölbe mit flachen Händen etwas fester klopfen...

...und antrocknen lassen!

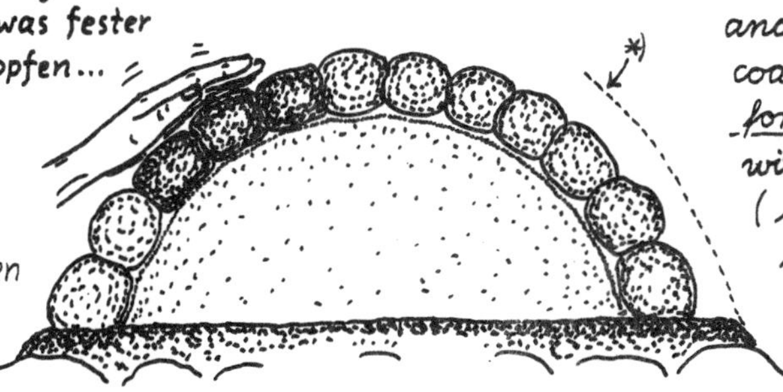

*) The oven will be better and more stable, if you coat it (dotted line) before removing the sand with a layer of adobe (loam with grass kneaded into it).

*) gestrichelte Linie: Noch besser und stabiler wird der Ofen, wenn Du vorm Ausräumen eine Schicht Graslehm (mit Lehmbrei durchkneteter Rasenschnitt) drumherum matschst.

3. Bau-Tag / 3rd construction day: Öffnungen hineinschneiden, Sand ausräumen!

Cut out openings and remove the sand, insert the stovepipe into the pointed end of the egg-

Stumpfes Ei-Ende: Türöffnung, passend zum Tür-Stein. Ränder mit Lehmschlamm glätten.

Make the door opening on the rounded end of the egg. Smooth the edges with loam-slurry.

Spitzes Ende: Ofenrohr einsetzen,...

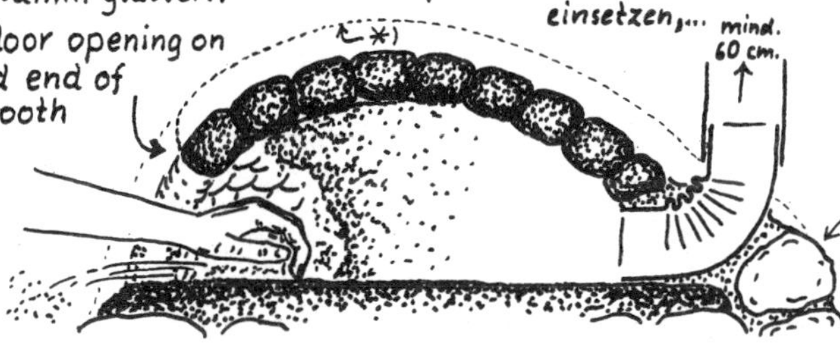

...oder Schlot aus Lehmbällen.

- or build a chimney from loam balls.

...und bald darfst Du zum ersten Mal heizen!

Loch, aus dem die Erde kam: darin kannst Du beim Heizen und Backen gut stehen!

Hole → where you dug up the building soil and which offers a good view of the fire hole when you're firing and baking.

Reisig zum Heizen
Brushwood for firing

Großer Stein zum Schließen der Türöffnung!
Large stone to close the fire-hole!

(30) Einfache Strohballenhütte, bewährt seit 1986!

Simple straw-bale hut, proven since 1986!

Bauweise: Strohballen auf 2 Knüppel legen, in Lehm-Wasser-Schlamm untertauchen und die vollgesaugten Ballen noch naß in Wand oder Decke verbauen.

Dip straw bales in loam-water-mixture; build walls or ceiling with the soaked bales while they are still wet.

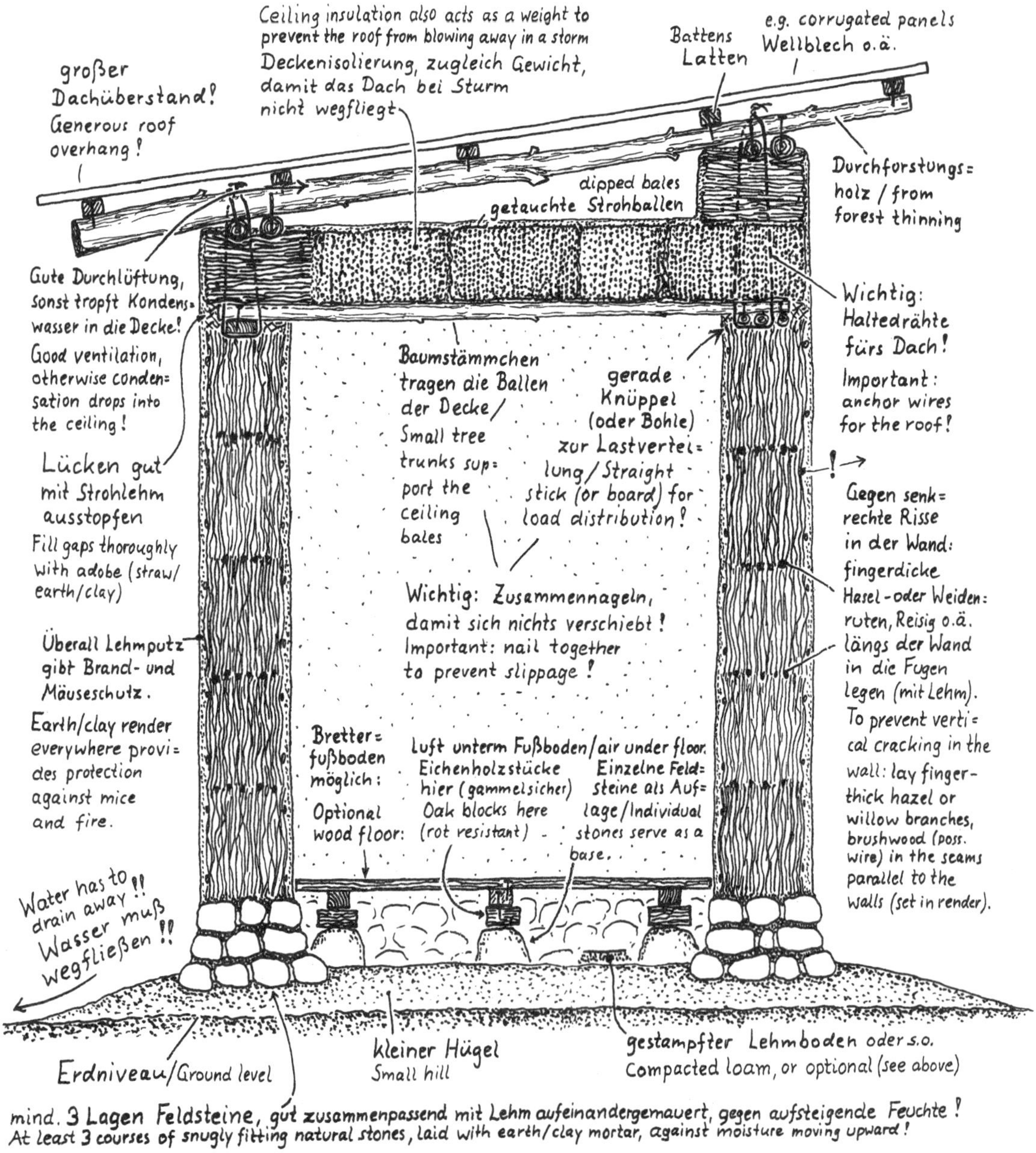

Einstöckige Strohballenbauten halten auch ohne Tragbalken in der Wand! Das vermeidet außerdem die Risse, die sonst zwischen Strohballen und Balken entstehen, weil die lehmgetränkten Ballen beim Trocknen schrumpfen. Nur oben lege zum Verteilen der Last der Deckenbalken Bohlen bzw mehrere lange gerade Knüppel nebeneinander auf die Wände. Eine Strohballenwand von 60 cm Dicke (2 Ballen hochkant nebeneinander oder ca 1 Ballen quer) hat schon etwa Niedrigenergiehaus-Standard und ist enorm tragfähig!

Single storey straw bale buildings do not require structural beams in the walls! This also eliminates the problem of cracks between straw bales and beams, caused when the walls shrink a couple of centimeters after drying. Simply lay planks (or several long, straight sticks parallel to one another) along the top the wall to distribute the load of the roof beams.
A 60 cm thick wall of straw bale (two adjacent bales standing on end or approx. 1 perpendicular bale)

Solange der Lehm noch nicht fest ist, müssen die Bänder viel halten!
The ties have to withstand a lot until the loam is dried up completely!

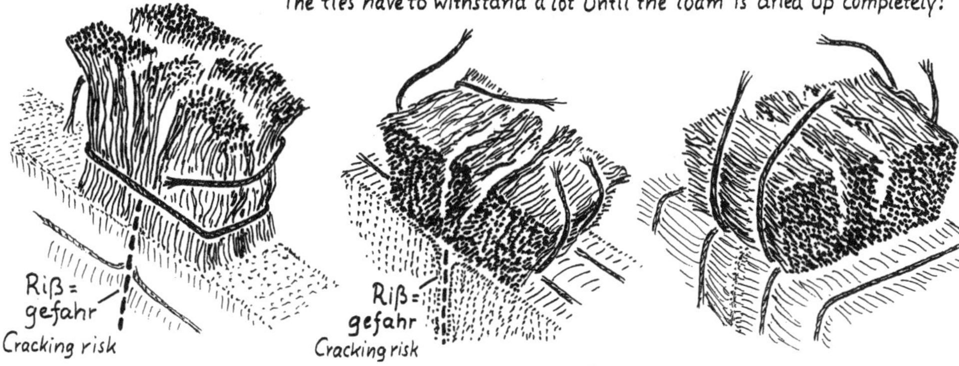

Strohhalme senkrecht: trägt am besten, aber der Ballen kann in allen Richtungen aufbrechen, schon wenn nur ein Band reißt.
Straw stalks vertical: Best load bearing but bales can split open in all directions, even when just a single tie snaps.

Halme liegend, quer zur Wand: Halme nachgiebiger, aber der Ballen kann nur quer zur Wand platzen. Gut unter längs auf der Wand liegenden Hölzern (Decken- od. Dachstuhl-Auflage).
Straw stalks perpendicular to walls: Straw more susceptible to compression, but bales can only split open perpendicular to the wall. Good under sticks laid parallel to the wall (ceilings or roof truss supports).

Halme liegend, längs der Wand: dicke Wand (für Wohnhäuser), sehr stabil. Ballen kann nur längs der Wand platzen. Deckenbalken auf die Mitte jedes Ballens legen und mit oben draufgenagelten Hölzern (z.B. Schwellenbalken) verbinden.
Stalks parallel to the wall: Thick walls (residental buildings), very stable. Bales can only split open parallel to the wall. Minimal cracking risk, stalks overlap parallel to the wall. Position ceiling beams directly upon the middle of each bale, connect the beams with threshold beams nailed ontop.

Vorsorge / safety measure:

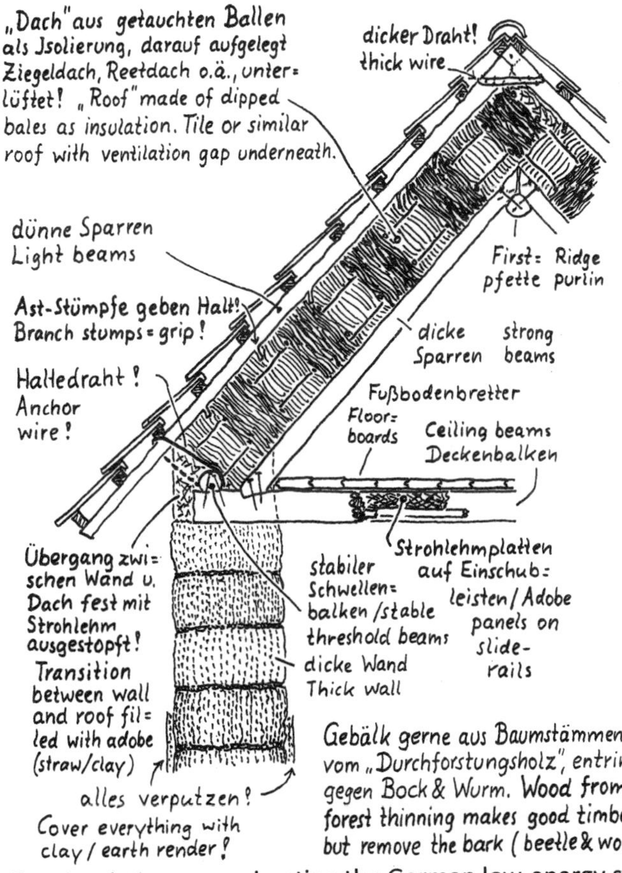

Construction tips for large and small structures:

Konstruktions-Tips für große und kleine Bauten.

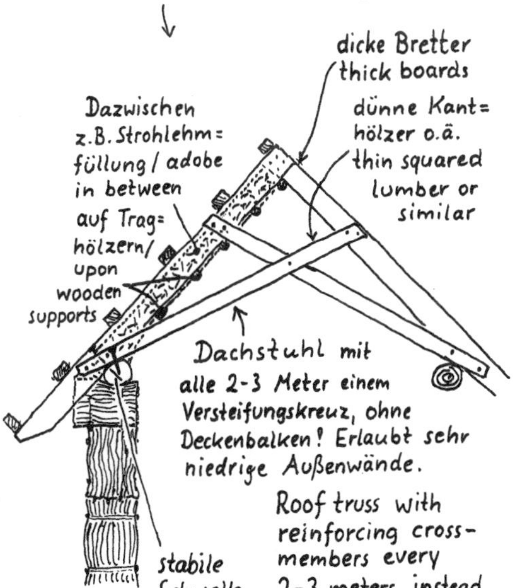

Roof truss with reinforcing cross-members every 2-3 meters, instead of ceiling beams. Allows very low exterior walls.

Gebälk gerne aus Baumstämmen vom „Durchforstungsholz", entrindet gegen Bock & Wurm. Wood from forest thinning makes good timbers, but remove the bark (beetle & worm).

Handwerk-Heft 3.

offers insulation approximating the German low-energy standard.

100 Notes – 100 Thoughts / 100 Notizen – 100 Gedanken

N°081: Christian Kuhtz
Trash Hacks / Einfälle statt Abfälle

dOCUMENTA (13), 9/6/2012 – 16/9/2012
Artistic Director / Künstlerische Leiterin: Carolyn Christov-Bakargiev
Member of Core Agent Group, Head of Department /
Mitglied der Agenten-Kerngruppe, Leiterin der Abteilung: Chus Martínez
Head of Publications / Leiterin der Publikationsabteilung: Bettina Funcke

Managing Editor / Redaktion und Lektorat: Katrin Sauerländer
Editorial Assistant / Redaktionsassistentin: Cordelia Marten
Coordination / Koordination: Stefanie Drobnik
English Copyediting / Englisches Lektorat: Melissa Larner
English Proofreading / Englisches Korrektorat: Sam Frank
Translation / Übersetzung: Timothy Hanes
Graphic Design and Typesetting / Grafische Gestaltung und Satz: Leftloft
Junior Graphic Designer: Daniela Weirich
Typeface / Schrift: Glypha, Plantin
Production / Verlagsherstellung: Maren Katrin Poppe
Reproductions / Reproduktionen: weyhing digital, Ostfildern
Paper / Papier: Pop'Set, 240 g/m², Munken Print Cream 15, 90 g/m²
Manufacturing / Gesamtherstellung: Dr. Cantz'sche Druckerei, Ostfildern

Illustrations / Abbildungen: p. / S. 1: View of / Ansicht des Monte Verità, ca. 1906 (detail / Detail), Fondo Harald Szeemann. Archivio Fondazione Monte Verità in Archivio di Stato del Cantone Ticino; all other images / alle anderen Abbildungen: © Christian Kuhtz

documenta und Museum Fridericianum
Veranstaltungs-GmbH
Friedrichsplatz 18, 34117 Kassel
Germany / Deutschland
Tel. +49 561 70727-0
Fax +49 561 70727-39
www.documenta.de
Chief Executive Officer / Geschäftsführer: Bernd Leifeld

Published by / Erschienen im
Hatje Cantz Verlag
Zeppelinstrasse 32, 73760 Ostfildern
Germany / Deutschland
Tel. +49 711 4405-200
Fax +49 711 4405-220
www.hatjecantz.com

ISBN 978-3-7757-2930-7 (Print)
ISBN 978-3-7757-3110-2 (E-Book)

Printed in Germany

Gefördert durch die

KULTURSTIFTUNG DES BUNDES

funded by the German Federal
Cultural Foundation